Doctor Robert Lefever

The Promis Rec

false medical gods

Written by Dr Robert Lefever

PROMIS Recovery Centre Limited
The Old Court House, Pinners Hill
Nonington, Nr. Canterbury
Kent CT15 4LL. UK
www.promis.co.uk

ISBN 1 871013 21 6

Design and production by Rainbow, Ipswich IP5 3RY, England.
Printed in Basauri, Spain by Grafo SA.

To my staff
and
to all who dare to think
and act for themselves

Acknowledgements

To my secretary Sarah Oaten for typing the manuscript,
to my editor, Dr Harriet Harvey Wood for her expertise,
to my proof reader, Keith Burns, for his skill,
and to my professional colleagues, patients, friends and family
who support me in my challenges to orthodoxy.

Contents

"What is actual is actual only for one time
And only for one place."

T.S. Eliot.

"The art of being wise is the art of knowing what to overlook."

William James.

"The process of changing a life-style is more important than reaching a goal or measuring a performance."

Theodore Isaac Rubin

"What wisdom can you find that is greater than kindness?"

Jean Jacques Rousseau.

Chapter One

Doctors in the USA and the UK

Good doctors anywhere, and of any age or either sex, deserve appreciation for the work they do – but so do architects or lawyers. If one is clever enough to get into a profession and to pass the examinations leading to professional registration, then surely it should be expected that one delivers the goods. This must be true of any profession. However, in medical practice there is an added factor: doctors have an almost unique capacity to heal or harm in equal measure. As a result, patients are often personally grateful for the technical work of doctors even though they know perfectly well that they should expect nothing less. Furthermore, patients are inevitably relatively poor judges of professional competence: they rarely have any comparable scientific educational base from which to make an informed critique. Added to that will be the fear of the unknown. Patients may sometimes revere their doctors because they dare not do otherwise.

In the USA, where doctors are called M.D.s, they are sometimes referred to as the M.Deity They are revered as gods and sometimes they see themselves as gods. However, with the advent of health maintenance organisations (H.M.O.s), the nearest thing the USA has to the United Kingdom's National Health Service, the status of American doctors is slipping: they are seen more as functionaries. Even so, outside the H.M.O.s, the top American specialists are mostly still running the medical "system", if not the hospitals, and they are appropriately respected: they are clever, they work incredibly hard and they save lives. In the UK National Health Service it is nowadays questionable whether top specialists even run their own departments. Administrators rule. UK specialists may have been gods at one time but they are certainly not now. General practitioners were never gods in either the USA or the UK except perhaps in televised fiction. The clinical and practical divide between general practitioners and specialists varies in other developed countries (in less privileged countries, patients may rarely see a doctor in their entire lives) but the USA and the UK represent the opposite ends of the spectrum.

One fundamental difference between the USA and UK is the route of access that patients have to follow in order to get specialist medical care. In the UK, general practitioners are the gatekeepers of the NHS, although some patients are able to get direct access to hospitals through Accident and Emergency Departments. In the USA the same is true to some extent but patients are also able to get direct access to consultant specialists. In many ways the distinction between general practitioners and consultant specialists is blurred in the USA. General practitioners often have special clinical interests and have admitting privileges to hospitals. By contrast in the UK, general practitioners may have particular clinical interests and may take part-time assistantships in hospital but most GPs work exclusively in their own offices in the community and will only venture into hospital in order to visit a patient personally, rather than to have any significant influence upon his or her treatment.

On both sides of the Atlantic GPs tend to be the poor relation of their specialist colleagues. Some consideration has been given in the past as to whether the profession should be divided right from the start in undergraduate training. The possible intention would be to train GPs for the work that they are most likely to do in clinical practice rather than have them spend many years of training in subjects that are of little practical relevance and, laboriously, in some disease processes that they will rarely see again. The rationale has been the belief that students have to be familiar with rare clinical conditions because otherwise they would misdiagnose them when they first see them in clinical practice.

There is something to be said for the Chinese "barefoot doctor" system in which a local villager is trained to recognise ten common ailments and provide simple treatment – and then refer up the line if the problem comes outside his or her range of expertise. The next tier works on the same general principle – and so on up various layers until at last the patient reaches a super-specialist. This "barefoot doctor" idea has not taken root in Western medical practice because doctors themselves like to control the entry of patients into the healthcare system. Equally the idea of training general medical practitioners separately from their specialist colleagues has not taken off because prospective students who are intellectually gifted tend to see the general practice option as having inferior status and therefore do not apply for that training.

Teaching hospitals in the USA and in the UK have tended to amalgamate, becoming progressively larger, so that medical students will have an opportunity to see a wide range of clinical conditions. In these enormous hospitals there are also financial economies of scale in the numbers of nurses and teaching staff. Medical education has become far more automated through the use of audiovisual aids, personal computers and access to the Internet but, as clinical practice becomes progressively more technical, so the medical students are trained progressively more to become technicians. Inevitably something is lost in this process. Patients may receive technical wizardry but may find that they are treated as "interesting cases" rather than as human beings.

In the USA the risk of malpractice suits has severely affected medical practice so that it is becoming progressively more defensive. Doctors may do unnecessary tests and procedures, and thereby significantly increase the cost of care, because they fear being sued catastrophically for negligence if they miss something. The exclusion of the possibility of rare diagnoses has become routine. Some of the tests that are performed in this process, which is self-protective for the doctors, are physically dangerous for their patients as well as being very expensive financially. The USA tends to be a litigious society at the best of times and never more so than when there is an opportunity for massive payouts from the errors of doctors or the pharmaceutical industry. Doctors' malpractice insurance premiums are now a very significant part of the cost of medical care in the USA. In the UK we are moving in the same direction but we have a long way to go to catch up.

In the USA recruitment into the medical profession is not as hotly contested today as it was twenty years ago. Bright young men are tending to want to become brokers or bankers or lawyers, partly because the financial rewards are now greater. More women are coming into the medical profession. That same trend is also observable in the UK and for the same reason: applications from men are falling.It is said that the status of a profession in the eyes of the public tends to fall as the proportion of women in that profession rises. This is obviously unfair to women. It is possible for women to rise to the top of the medical professional ladder on both sides of the Atlantic and some do so with considerable distinction. However, there are many exceedingly able women who do not rise to the same professional levels as their male counterparts. In part this is a product of male chauvinism and the "old boy network". However, in the current social organisation of our countries there is also a biological factor: women tend to take time out to have children and to look after them when they are young. Some women doctors never return to clinical practice after having children. Others find it hard to pick up the academic reins from where they left off many years previously and they may also find it difficult to accept the onslaught of on-call arrangements while also caring for a young family. Where on-call arrangements are delegated to agencies, rather than to specific doctors, the relationship between doctor and patient becomes less personal. Again the direction of change is in clinical practice becoming more technical and less vocational or pastoral.

Some women consultant specialists are single but many are not. Those who are married have often had a double battle to fight: one at home and the other at work. Even in general practice the requirements of full-time work can be very demanding in terms of time and energy and for this reason many married women work part-time. The end result is that the status of this branch of the profession tends to slide even further. General medical practice is sometimes seen progressively less as a "proper" job in a clinical speciality and more as a branch of social work.

Not that life is altogether a bed of roses for men. Competition in the medical profession is still severe both in the USA and in the UK, and the technical aspects of undergraduate and postgraduate examinations can be exceedingly demanding. Those of us who took our last examination two or three decades ago view our junior colleagues with admiration and we reflect upon the prospect of our own revalidation assessments with apprehension. Gone are the days when older doctors were revered. Today they are assumed to be out-of-date and even incompetent until they prove otherwise. Older doctors may have been gods – or at least folk heroes – in previous years but no longer.

The greatest trap in deifying the medical profession, however, is when we – the members of the medical profession – do it to ourselves. It is when we ourselves believe that we are gods that we are likely to make the most serious errors in clinical practice and in interpersonal communication. There is an appropriate distance between doctor and patient but the doctor should approach the relationship with an appropriate level of humility. The doctor who is over-familiar does not give confidence in moments of crisis. On the other hand, the doctor who postures and pontificates and who has no sense of personal or professional humility should also cause significant concern if one has to trust one's life to him or her. In each case these "gods" can become dangerous precisely because they may be unchallenged by their patients or by their colleagues in their personal attitudes. Neither doctors nor patients can afford that – in the USA, the UK or anywhere else.

Chapter Two

Scientific Classification and Research

The "scientific method", taking only whatever actions are supported by research evidence, is central to clinical practice. It is right that it should be. However, its limitations are rarely acknowledged.

Medical periodicals, the magazines read by doctors, tend to fall into two discrete camps. The content of the first, such as *The British Medical Journal* or *Lancet* or the various specialist periodicals relevant to each clinical discipline such as cardiology or gastroenterology, is mainly research papers. The content of the second, such as *Pulse, GP Magazine, Doctor* or *Hospital Doctor*, is partly clinical and partly political, often dealing with issues concerning doctors' pay and conditions of service. In both these groups of medical journals there are correspondence columns but rarely in either is there the opportunity to float a clinical idea. Between number-crunching research and mind-numbing petty politics there is no room for true originality. This is a great loss to clinical practice.

In the broader scientific field in Thomas Gold's book, *The Deep Hot Biosphere* (Copernicus 1998) there is a dramatic example of how one new idea could completely revolutionise standard thinking. Dr Gold is a fellow of the British Royal Society and a member of the American Academy of Sciences and is therefore established as one of the top scientists in the world. In this book he argues firstly that coal and oil are not fossil fuels like peat but are part of the geological structure of the earth from elements that are common throughout the universe. Secondly he believes that life began deep inside the earth and it continues to be created there to this day. He says that surface life is relatively recent. The book is fascinating – but what is important to my argument is that Dr Gold, by looking at things in a new way rather than going over old accepted ideas, may show that all our previous thoughts on the subject were wrong. Now imagine that same principle being applied, for example, to the ideas of Sigmund Freud. Nowadays, Freud's ideas are often believed with the tenacity of religious fervour. One 'scientific' paper after another on psychoanalysis may be consistent with others on the same subject but I believe that the whole lot may be based upon a false premise.

Human beings are individual. There is a great deal that we have in common with each other but there are also some aspects of each individual that are unique. To reduce everything to numbers in clinical research papers inevitably produces the lowest common denominator. It may be useful to know that 75% of the population react in a particular way – to an illness or to a pharmaceutical substance – but we should not overlook the fact that 25% do not. Further, the reasons why they do not react in the same way may be very varied, just as the reasons why the 75% did react in the same way may also not necessarily be identical. Numbers do not tell the whole picture. To be sure they tell us something, but they don't tell everything and it is surely the great mysteries of life that should be the most fascinating. Crunching everything down into little bits that can be counted and cross-referenced and analysed destroys something of the bigger picture. Counting is good but thinking is better. Music is something more than dots on a manuscript. There is something in the way that component parts work in conjunction with each other that is lost when they are taken apart and examined individually. The numbers may be right – there is a precise number of cogs in a wheel – but that does not necessarily tell us precisely how the wheel functions in all circumstances. It may have different functions at different times or in different places. Surely that is what really matters.

Scientists tend to be well aware of this and they may even categorise themselves as "splitters" or "lumpers". The first group tends always to split everything down into its component parts whereas the second group builds up the parts as far as possible towards a coherent whole. There is something to be said for both approaches but neither gives the full picture on its own.

The authors and editors of research papers sometimes fall into the trap of believing that research results *prove* something. They do not: they simply lead to a hypothesis that seems to be the most accurate within our current understanding. Indeed, there are occasions when two theoretical models, each internally consistent, are in conflict with each other. For example, Newtonian physics and quantum theory are both obviously "right" in so far as each has precise formulae from which one can make specific deductions. However, Newtonian physics and quantum theory cannot both be right in all circumstances: there are some particular concepts that are mutually contradictory. If this principle is true for inorganic inanimate matter, then how much more must it be true for the explanations that we provide for the behaviour of organic molecules and the complex organisms of life? The greatest danger in all science is to believe at any time that we know all the answers. The true scientist acknowledges that he or she knows only some of the questions.

Medical research is particularly important because clinical decisions may be taken as a result of believing the data. Patients' lives may be influenced for better or worse. The issue here is not simply concern for fraudulent research – that most despicable of all clinical events – but of reading more into the numbers than may be justifiable. A particular set of figures may lead one towards a particular conclusion but is that the only possible conclusion and what would be the circumstances in which it might not be true? These would be the mental processes of a true scientist – and indeed that is precisely how progress is commonly made – but the pseudo-scientists, who fill medical journals with publications purely and simply in order to be able to record on their curriculum vitae that they have done so, may have little insight into what scientific method is really about. Karl Popper's *Philosophy of Science* may be literally a closed book to them.

There is a very real problem when professional promotion depends not upon technical skill nor communicative ability nor even upon individual commitment or compassion but on publication of research papers. Are these really the doctors whom we want to promote to positions of authority in clinical practice and in medical schools? They may be clever – in their way – but is that really enough? It could be argued that research papers provide a measure of quantifiable assessment whereas the other factors that I have mentioned are too nebulous. This is countered by the challenge that Professor Lawrence Weed of the University of Vermont puts to us in his book, *Medical Records, Medical Education and Patient Care* (Yearbook Publications 1969). In this he points out that the question repeatedly asked of medical students tends to be "what do you know?" rather than "how would you work it out?"

The answer to the first question is easy to mark in an examination. The answers to the second question may be infinitely more revealing and much more relevant to clinical practice – but assessing it requires effort. The end result of this obsession with the question "what do you know?" is that assessors for publication in medical periodicals, just as much as for appointments to professional positions, tend to go for the easier option and allow themselves to be taken in by numbers, graphs, bar charts, statistics and heaven knows what else. All these things have a proper place but I question whether they should have the dominant place that they have currently achieved in the promotion of doctors to higher professional appointments.

The alternative to acting on instinct has obvious drawbacks. It is true that patients deserve something better than guesswork, hunch, whim or even prejudice from their doctors. Even so, a "sixth sense" based on clinical experience is not something to be lightly dismissed. A simple "feel" on whether or not the patient is ill is something that any clinician should develop in the course of his or her professional work. Our patients are not robots. Nor are we. We can use computers to assist us with diagnosis and treatment – reminding us of what we might otherwise forget – but we cannot be replaced by them altogether. Clinical judgement has a place – particularly when the numbers don't seem to fit – even though they are "correct". Surely clinical judgement is what we should most value in a doctor, rather than the number of research papers to his or her name.

The medical periodicals that are more political in content have an important part to play. They remind us that the very same scientific number-crunching pedant may also be preoccupied by issues concerning his or her remuneration or entitlements under an employment contract. At times those issues become so overwhelming that they may blur dispassionate clinical judgement. A doctor who is tired or dispirited or angry may have excellent scientific credentials but still do terrible work with his or her patients. One way or another, if we worship the God of scientific measurement and research, we may have excellent reasons for doing so – but there are also some excellent reasons for looking at the broader picture and *not* closing our eyes in blind faith in this particular God.

Chapter Three

Teaching Hospitals

One would have thought that the primary function of a teaching hospital would be to teach medical students and postgraduates. Would that that were true!

Teaching hospitals are no different from other universities: their prime function is for the staff to reproduce themselves. Teaching is merely the tedious requirement that is attached to salaries. There are some excellent teachers – in the eyes of the undergraduate and postgraduate students – but they are not necessarily valued in the eyes of their peers. They may even be looked down upon, if not actually despised.

Communicative skills are rarely valued as highly as the capacity to oversee a research project. At times, in collegiate systems, they may be valued significantly less than the capacity to oversee the institution's wine cellar. At a level of even greater concern, it is said that there are some London teaching hospitals where membership of a Masonic lodge is a prerequisite before appointment to the consultant staff.

Be that as it may, I am none-the-less unaware of any undergraduate or postgraduate institution where teachers are selected *primarily* on their ability to teach. This is bizarre. It is comparable to appointing musicians to an orchestra or choir when they can neither play nor sing with any significant competence. Teaching is a practical skill and the undergraduate and postgraduate students deserve access to people who possess that skill. The research programmes of universities should be conducted by research staff – not teaching staff – and, correspondingly, teaching staff should teach, not do research. The two functions are different, and should be given equal weight, yet somehow teaching has become the poor relation. But what could be more important than helping to train young minds in a way that preserves freshness and enthusiasm? A good teacher can have a lasting effect for decades whereas a researcher who becomes dispirited may make a professorial chair into a bed.

The prime drawback with teaching hospitals, it appears to me, is whether they should exist at all at the undergraduate level. Surely the principal function of undergraduate training is to ensure that medical students become familiar with the clinical conditions that they are *most* likely to meet in practice. They should learn how to examine hearts and lungs and feel for enlarged livers and kidneys. They should see varicose veins and hernias, cataracts and perforated eardrums. They should follow through a normal pregnancy. They should see prolapses and haemorrhoids. They should be familiar with sadness as well as schizophrenia. They may indeed see all these conditions in teaching hospitals at present – but are they valued as the stuff of real life? Or are they scorned as "trivia" while clinical rarities are prized?

Half the product of teaching hospitals will work in general medical practice, seeing common things commonly. If they have been trained, deliberately or inadvertently, to despise the clinically commonplace, they will come to despise their daily work and possibly even themselves. This is a terrible price to pay for the elitism of teaching hospitals that believe that the "successes" of their training programme are typified by the students who won prizes and who stayed in hospital work – and in due course became teaching hospital consultants themselves.

In my view students should primarily be trained to be as accurate as they can be in their clinical examination of patients and then learn to look things up and ask questions when they don't know the answer to any particular problem. There should be nothing humiliating about asking a question when one does not know the answer: that should be a source of pride. If teaching hospitals could inspire their students with that principle, it would be an excellent start to a professional career in clinical practice.

I can well understand the need for postgraduate teaching hospitals where future specialists are learning the specific tools of their trade. My concern over undergraduate teaching hospitals is that they take students too fast towards specialisation whereas what they most need is breadth of experience and understanding rather than depth in any particular area. The best places to learn about the general rough and tumble of clinical practice must surely be in general rough and tumble hospitals and in general medical practice. Students should do their academic learning in universities – and patients can be brought to them to demonstrate particular clinical features or syndromes – but they should learn the basics from the doctors who are doing the basic work. They can graduate (whether one considers it a step up or a step down or a step across is a matter of opinion) to ivory-tower specialist institutions at a later date. With luck they will never forget the needs of the general population and will never seek to acquire that most hallowed of all medical accolades: the eponym, the rare clinical condition named after the doctor who first described it and who did the most good to the fewest people.

false medical gods

Chapter Four

Medical Institutions

The British Medical Association is a trade union pure and simple. Primarily it represents NHS doctors in negotiations with the Government over fees and conditions of service.

There is a private practice committee of the BMA but fully private doctors themselves very rarely, if ever, have anything to do with it because they have better things to do with their time – such as earning money from the care of patients. The private practice committee mainly deals with those aspects of NHS doctors' work that are not covered in the standard terms of service in their contracts – such as fees for certifying someone fit to drive a heavy goods vehicle or for providing a report to the Coroner or for the Social Security overlords.

In essence the BMA is a political institution. Through publishing an excellent journal, the *British Medical Journal*, it might have some pretensions towards improving the quality of medical care in the UK but its main function, like that of any other trade union, is to represent the interests of its members by claiming more pay for less work and threatening severe consequences if its "evidence" (on the dire state of its members' financial plight and working conditions) is not met with an "appropriate" response from Government. The majority of NHS doctors are members of this trade union – but not all.

I myself was once a member of the BMA when I was in full-time NHS practice and I went so far as to be a representative on the Inner London Local Medical Committee. In that exalted position members of the committee discussed important issues such as whether a protein supplement should be classified as a food or as a drug. As a food the patient would have to pay for it whereas in the case of a drug the NHS, in its wisdom and bounty, would provide. I am sure there were more significant issues that we discussed but I don't remember them. What I do remember is that when I proposed that the BMA should press the Government to provide GPs with better access to hospital diagnostic facilities, such as x-ray departments and pathology laboratories, I was told that this was an interesting idea that I might well like to put forward again when I was more senior.

Now, as a GP in fully private practice, I have nothing to gain from membership of the BMA other than free copies of the *British Medical Journal*. Interestingly the cost of BMJ to non-members is the same as the cost of membership of the Association itself. I believe this must be because the BMA recognises that its true stature in the profession is as the publisher of the *BMJ*.

The Royal Colleges (of physicians, surgeons, obstetricians and gynaecologists, pathologists, general practitioners and what-have-you, each discipline having its own) are not so much concerned with politics – although all life is politics – but with clinical standards. Membership of a college is usually by examination, set by the college itself, and the candidates who pass the examination – in specialist fields other than general practice – are generally accepted to be suitable candidates for consultant posts in hospital and to have their consultation fees to private patients reimbursed by private medical insurance companies. Some general practice partnerships expect incoming partners to be members of the Royal College of General Practitioners but this is far from universal.

In my view the Royal Colleges are basically on the side of the angels, looking to improve the standard of clinical care for patients. The problem comes not from the colleges themselves but from some of the individual members who, on the strength of their membership of a Royal College, give themselves airs and graces as important human beings, lording it over lesser mortals. Merely on the basis of the professional examination that they passed in their twenties or thirties, they convince themselves that they are for ever more a separate species. I have no difficulty in admiring the portraits of former presidents of the Royal Colleges that now adorn their establishments. These doctors were elected to those posts by their peers on the strength of the distinction that they had brought to the profession. The immortality of a portrait is a worthy, innocent reward. I do have difficulty, however, with the doctors who wear the badge of their college membership for all to admire from the day they acquired it to the day they retire - and beyond - without ever doing anything original or even, at times, industrious. Their professional appointments often have lifetime tenure and they may see no reason, on the strength of their college membership, why they should ever work to prove anything again. Passing the college membership examination was the pinnacle of their professional achievement. This is an extraordinarily impoverished state of mind and must surely be the opposite of the ethos that created the Royal Colleges.

Progression to Fellowship of the Royal Colleges is by election and is a worthy accolade. As with the financial "merit awards", given by the NHS to some top consultant specialists on the suggestion of their peers as a mark of professional value (and often as a recognition of their dedication to the NHS because they could generally earn more money in private practice), there is an occasional hint of an exclusive club but that is, for the most part, an innocent conceit. Where it may not be altogether innocent is when the same doctors become advisors to the private medical insurance companies and determine which procedures and which doctors and institutions should receive their financial support. When these same NHS doctors also have appointments in private hospitals and when there is transfer of NHS-funded patients to treatment in the private sector, there is the possibility of the whiff of financial chicanery or, at any rate, a hint of "you scratch my back and I'll scratch yours". That is unacceptable.

Medical insurance companies are a significant force in their own right. Although only 14% of the population of the UK has private medical insurance cover, this is nonetheless a very significant number of people, and they bring with them very significant financial clout. Mostly the medical insurance companies grew out of provident institutions in which the weekly contributions of individual members were pooled and then given out to those who had fallen on difficult times. Their successors, the present-day medical insurance companies, might like us to believe that they still function on the same principle. In practice, they do not: they are strictly commercial in their operation and they do whatever they can to put up their income and reduce their costs. As patients get older, their premiums rise because of the greater risk of illness. Patients who develop chronic illnesses often find that the small print of their policies soon diverts them back to the understandably resentful arms of the NHS. Deductibles (where the patient has to pay an initial sum) or exclusions (where some conditions are not covered at all) or other limitations (such as commonly apply in psychiatric conditions where there may be a limit to the length of time of hospital cover on one occasion or in any one year or even where cover may be limited to one episode in a lifetime) conspire to ensure that the medical insurance companies rarely provide long-term cover. They tend to wriggle out of long-term commitments wherever they possibly can. While posturing as an alternative clinical service to the NHS, they are in fact no such thing. Furthermore, when they themselves own private hospitals - which they do in considerable number - they generally avoid the training of medical and nursing staff, preferring to pinch the ready-trained staff from the NHS. Most of their clinical work is in creaming off the relatively straightforward and predictable procedures - such as surgical operations that can largely be quantified in their costs. One can understand patients wanting to have the best possible care and, if they can afford it, being prepared to pay for it on top of the contributions to the NHS that they pay through their taxes. However, while purporting to help the NHS, doctors who work in both the state system and the private sector in fact undermine the NHS when they take time away from their NHS patients. It is an unattractive picture.

The Health Maintenance Organisations in the USA are no different and, in a remarkable double, sometimes achieve the worst of our own NHS and private sectors. The future is likely to be worse on both sides of the Atlantic as the private medical insurance companies bankrupt competing institutions by withdrawing their cover and by leaving the beleaguered state systems to provide care for those patients who most need it and who have least capacity to provide for themselves. This type of "two-tier" system is the stuff of which revolutions are made and rightly so. Doctors who say that private practice gives them the opportunity to give the "proper" amount of time to the care of their patients seem to have no idea that, where there is a fixed number of doctors, increased time given to one patient necessarily deprives another.

The General Medical Council (GMC) mostly comes into public view when errant doctors come before its disciplinary committee. However, its custodianship of the medical register is just as important when considering whom to put on it as whom to remove from it. In this way the GMC monitors the standards of medical student training both in the UK and abroad so that doctors trained in the UK are ensured to have reached a particular standard and doctors trained elsewhere often have to submit to further assessment if they apply to work in the UK.

Temporarily suspending, or altogether removing, doctors' names from the medical register is a vitally important role for the GMC in the protection of patients. In recent years there have been some dramatic failures in this custodial role. Doctors who have butchered or even murdered their patients have apparently been able to do so for many years before the GMC has woken up to what is going on. Of course the GMC can only act on the information that it receives and the medical profession itself may sometimes close ranks rather than report its errant members.

The greater powers now given to the health committee of the GMC, who recognise that the actions of some doctors are not so much wicked as sick, was a great advance in helping the GMC to have a more appropriate compassionate face than one that was judge, jury and executioner all in one. Even so, the medical profession is, in my view, still very poor at policing itself. The "three wise men" system in hospitals, in which concerns may be expressed to these chosen senior colleagues over the behaviour of other doctors, exists but that does not mean that it is used to any great extent. Furthermore, doctors who have ultimately expressed concern - as in the Bristol Cardiac Surgery Unit - may be given a very rough ride. In general practice there is no equivalent to the "three wise men" system and there is cold comfort when one asks for advice.

In recent years concern has been expressed over the constitution of the GMC: it has largely been run by doctors and it was seen to be overly defensive of them and inadequate in their supervision. When Dr Harold Shipman was found to have been a mass murderer of staggering proportions over a considerable number of years, there was understandable public concern on how he had not been picked up earlier. If the GMC did not protect patients from being murdered by their doctors, then what did it do? The end result of this case in particular, but also of others that caused great public concern, is that the GMC has now brought in a system of revalidation for doctors so that we have to prove our fitness to practise and therefore our right to remain on the medical register. Previously registration continued automatically until removed from us on retirement or as a result of being caught in the rather porous net of the GMC disciplinary committee. This change is all to the good. The process of revalidation is tedious - but so it should be. It won't pick up every possible mistake but these checks and balances never can (a fact that is sometimes completely ignored by the press, Parliament and the public). At any rate, those of us who have the privilege of being on the medical register should acknowledge that it is a privilege rather than a God-given right and therefore we should be answerable to the people who grant us that privilege - ultimately our patients and those who represent them.

Perhaps the patients' representatives on the GMC now have too much power. The advent of patient power in general practice advisory groups and the various tiers of local health authorities (these organisations change their names with disconcerting frequency but the same people tend to turn up time and again wearing slightly different hats) is not altogether the good thing that it is sometimes made out to be. The Soviet experience of mountains of bureaucracy but appalling clinical services should be a warning to us all.

The current level of disillusion and despair within the medical profession in all branches of the NHS is not something that society can afford to ignore. There comes a time when the search for "bad" doctors disturbs the work of the "good". Having authorities of one kind or another constantly breathing down a doctor's neck is not conducive to making fewer mistakes: it makes them more likely. Doctors do not deserve to be treated as gods – but neither are they devils. When the chairman of a health authority – one of the "great and good" appointed to this important position – recently referred to the hospital doctors under his supervision as "the enemy", he showed himself, in my view, to be unworthy of his position.

Under such assaults, it is not surprising that doctors occasionally wonder who will be on their side; who will defend them. In technical terms we are defended by our malpractice insurance organisations. I personally have found the advisers of the Medical Protection Society extremely helpful to me when discussing the potential pitfalls (there are many and various) in running an addiction treatment centre. It might be imagined that if I – or any other doctor – should err, then these professional indemnity organisations would automatically defend us. This is not true. Their annual reports show time and again when they have considered a doctor's actions to be indefensible. In this particular respect, as in many others right across the whole spectrum of medical practice, doctors can be seen to be policing themselves successfully at least to some extent if not perfectly.

All these various medical institutions were established primarily to protect patients and serve them and they were all largely established on the initiative of doctors themselves. If, in the name of progress or accountability or democracy, doctors become harried or hunted, they will inevitably react. The profession deserves to be judged by its best members and by their good intentions as well as by their worst. If we see ourselves as gods we will fly too close to the sun and deservedly meet the same fate as Icarus. If other people treat us as gods then we would be silly to believe them. If they try to make us into gods, expecting infallibility, we have no chance of achieving that and we shall become progressively more defensive in our actions. The pendulum may swing from one extreme to the other but neither extreme is healthy for patients, their doctors or for the medical system of the country. Our various medical institutions, if they have any value at all, should focus time and energy on discovering, protecting and enhancing the best clinical practice as they do in rooting out the worst. But this can only be achieved in a spirit of cooperation rather than confrontation.

Chapter Five

Medical Ethics

It may seem strange for medical ethics to be considered a false medical god but the subject is not as clear-cut as might first appear.

Medical ethics is not a static subject: no medical advance can ever take place without challenging our existing system of medical ethics. The current concerns over genetic engineering and cloning come hot on the heels of similar concerns over abortion, *in vitro* fertilisation and stem-cell research. They in turn followed concerns over the decision to resuscitate the terminally ill and that particular issue still has echoes today when considering patients' "rights" to voluntary euthanasia. (I question this right because the right to die is not the same as the right to require someone else to kill.)

The basic concept of the sanctity of human life is now challenged to breaking point. As the Pope points out, contraception – other than the singularly unsafe "rhythm method" which involves having intercourse at a time of the month when eggs are hopefully not around to be fertilised – is an artificial interference in the process of procreation. The Pope is undoubtedly right: living semen finish up in a blind alley in a condom or against a contraceptive cap, spermicidal jellies mean that they are prevented from fertilising the ovum, an intra-uterine device causes the possible abortion of a fertilised ovum every month, and the pill or an injection of hormones alters the natural female menstrual cycle so that eggs are not produced. In every case, science is used to distort nature.

The alternative would be to return to the days of multiple pregnancies, putting an immense social strain and limitation upon the lives of women, or to the days of frequent "backstreet" abortions. Clearly many women look at the practicalities of their lives and question whether contraception or abortion really is unethical. It could be argued – and often is – that this simply illustrates that ethical standards are slipping. However, there is a perfectly reasonable alternative argument, which is that standards may need to change. Nonetheless, the fact that so many women still get pregnant today and subsequently request termination of pregnancy, even though contraception is readily available to them prior to or even at the time of copulation or after it, indicates that we may have become disturbingly casual in our consideration of ethical principles. Women who have recurrent abortions, using them almost as a method of contraception, may have a psychological problem in their relationship with reality, hoping one moment that they can avoid it and then the next moment having to face up to it. At the same time their male partners have clearly not given appropriate thought to their own responsibility in causing an unwanted pregnancy. The advent of the contraceptive pill certainly changed the sexual practices of a generation – but it also changed the ethics. Who are we – now or then – to say that it should not do so?

On the other hand are we prepared to give science full rein? Should lesbians be given artificial insemination so that they can give birth to children? Should homosexual male couples be allowed to adopt? Who are we in the heterosexual community to make rules for lesbian and gay couples simply because of an accident of fate, possibly genetic, that leads them to have a sexual persuasion that would not enable them to have children "normally"? Should they not also be given the benefit of scientific advances just as heterosexual couples reap the benefit of *in vitro* fertilisation when their own bodies have been found to be incapable of reproducing themselves? Who is now to say that some women are "too old" to have children simply because they are post-menopausal? Who is to say that a young girl with significant mental impairment should be required to have an abortion? Who would say that another young girl made pregnant by a rape should not do so? The issues are not at all straightforward.

Nature abhors a vacuum and human nature follows suit. As soon as difficult issues arise it can be guaranteed that someone ("Rent-an-opinion") will step forward with an "obvious" solution to the difficulties. He or she usually supports his or her opinion by claiming that something or other is "ethical" or "unethical". It is not – or, at least, it may be so only according to that particular person's ethics.

When Christopher Reeve, the actor known particularly for his role as "Superman" and now paralysed from the neck down as the result of a horse-riding accident, reflected upon the prospect of using stem-cell research to provide a nerve tissue graft that would possibly enable him to walk again, he acknowledged that he might have to leave the USA, where such treatments are considered unethical, and travel to the UK where they are considered ethical. The Italian gynaecologist, who is happy to make post-menopausal women become pregnant through *in vitro* fertilisation, is seen as a saint by some and a sinner by others. The prospect of cloning embryonic tissue so as to establish a bank for possible "spare-part" surgery is greeted with horror by some and excitement by others. Precisely when does life begin? Precisely where do we draw the line in using scientific techniques in the relief of suffering? Should we use aborted foetuses for the possible good that could be done through implanting their nerve tissue into the brains of people suffering from Parkinson's disease – or should we simply incinerate or bury them? The issues seem totally simple – and glaringly obvious – to some, but not to others.

The real issue of contention that I myself have with "Rent-an-opinion" is that he or she, in the absolutely firm conviction of his or her own viewpoint, usually expects me, as a doctor, to do his or her bidding. He or she makes the decisions but I then have to take the actions. A group of them may even form a committee of the great and the good, the wise, well educated and usually well known – and then they tell me what I should do or not do. They would claim that I am "unethical" if I take an action according to my own beliefs (leaving aside for the moment the issue of whether the action was legal or otherwise) but they would have no qualms over expecting me to do something at their behest even if it was contrary to my own beliefs. They might accuse me of arrogance or of assuming God-like powers if I were to refuse to do what they wanted me to do on the grounds that I did not myself believe in it. What ethics are these that they would wish me to follow? Perhaps the doctors who worked for Hitler or Stalin were able to bury their own consciences – but theirs is hardly an ethical principle that we should encourage other doctors to follow. Yet that principle – at a lesser but not necessarily trivial level – is precisely what "ethical committees" may set themselves up to promote.

Examining the issue of whether or not something is legal is no answer to the ethical dilemma in which doctors may find themselves. For example, it is legal for me to procure an abortion – but I shall never do it myself. Yet in referring a patient for a termination of pregnancy, I acknowledge the ethical responsibility for my decision and I acknowledge that I am to all intents and purposes doing the termination myself in every way but physical. I therefore have ethical responsibilities for the action. Ultimately doctors cannot have the privilege of separating our ethical principles from our capacity to act. Nor, in my view, can other people claim the right to have ethical principles and then expect doctors to put them into practice.

In response to the expectation of "Rent-an-opinion" that I should use the scalpel or turn off the switch in accordance with his or her principles, I would say, "Here's the scalpel. There's the switch. You do it". This may seem arrogant but I would call it ethical: the responsibility goes with the job. It is what we took on when we became doctors. Furthermore, I believe that it would be totally unethical for doctors to discuss the practicalities of these issues outside their own ranks. I would even go so far as to say that the only doctors who should make decisions on ethical issues are those who are in active clinical practice. We are not gods, but we do have specific responsibilities that we cannot share.

Chapter Six

Pharmacology and Therapeutics

Just because something *can* be done does not mean necessarily that it *should* be done. New drugs and treatments are changing the face of medical practice every year and it is wonderful that they should do so. However, their use by doctors is a choice rather than a command.

There are essentially three issues when doctors consider prescribing a drug or some other form of therapy:

i. Does the patient need this treatment at all?
ii. Will the potential benefits outweigh the risks?
iii. Is it appropriate to use a limited resource – in terms either of cost or of availability – on this particular patient, bearing in mind the potential benefit for this patient as opposed to others?

The first question is a challenge to the concept of "a pill for every ill". In this, patients and doctors tend to collude in the general principle, if not over specific treatments. For example, NHS doctors tend to be very reluctant to prescribe antibiotics for coughs and colds. What they say is that the use of antibiotics should be reserved for proven bacterial infections and that over-prescribing results in an increasing pool of resistant organisms. What they may really mean is that patients should not waste the doctor's time with "trivia". The ideal clinical course in this situation is to take a swab of the infected throat or nose and wait for the culture to be reported on by the pathology staff before prescribing an antibiotic that can be shown from that culture to be specifically effective in killing the particular infecting organism. The problem is that this process takes two or three days and is not as accurate as it is sometimes made out to be. Samples can get lost, or contaminating organisms from the laboratory itself may grow on the culture plate. Even when the correct organism is identified, an antibiotic which is effective in a laboratory culture may not necessarily be equally effective when it is given to the patient. While it is true that over-prescribing of broad spectrum antibiotics in the hospital environment results, in that closed atmosphere, in the generation of resistant organisms, the same is not true in general practice in the open community. Patients sometimes misunderstand this general principle of resistance in natural organisms and believe that it is they themselves rather than the microbes who become resistant to the antibiotic. NHS doctors who merely want to reduce the number of patient consultations and cut down on their workload often do nothing to dispel that misconception.

It is a good general principle to prescribe antibiotics only when absolutely necessary but, on the other hand, it has to be said that the "over-prescription" of antibiotics has probably been a very significant factor in virtually abolishing the incidence of rheumatic fever – and subsequent rheumatic heart disease. Indiscriminate prescription of antibiotics may also prevent occasional potentially devastating effects of secondary infection elsewhere in the body by the common cause of sore throats, a *beta haemolytic streptococcus*. "Bad" doctors may inadvertently be doing "good" work!

On the same principle of "a pill for every ill", doctors, in my view, tend to be far too ready to prescribe psychotropic drugs such as anti-psychotics, tranquillisers, anti-depressants and sleeping tablets. Again there may be a difference between what doctors say and what they may mean. By saying, "I am sure this can help you", they may mean, "I would not know what to do if deprived of my prescription pad". They do sometimes openly acknowledge that they do not have time to deal with the emotional and social problems of their patients but this strikes me as being very short-sighted: the emotional and social problems of today often become the physical problems of tomorrow. In any case, time is a function of organisation and delegation and also of clinical interest. Many of the clinical conditions upon which doctors do spend their time in general medical practice could easily be delegated to nurses after the doctor has made the initial assessment. (However, in the USA the predictable result of nurse practitioners doing the work in place of doctors was that they soon demanded the income of the doctors.) In my own case, throughout the whole of my professional life I have *wanted* to see patients for their emotional problems because I believe that this is a major responsibility of GPs. We can refer on to consultant specialists when patients develop physical problems, and we can refer mental problems to psychiatrists, but the appropriate management of emotional problems, for which I believe doctors vastly over-prescribe drugs, should be within the counselling skills of GPs. After all, what patients most want is often no more than a listening ear and I believe that that is exactly what they deserve rather than pharmaceutical drugs, about whose action on the delicate tissues of the brain we really know very little.

In hospitals the problems that arise from pharmaceutical prescription tend to come from two sources: firstly, the use of multiple medications comes as a direct result of doctors being trained primarily to prescribe; and, secondly, turf wars between competing specialities. Jockeying for status and funds tends to be expressed pharmacologically on the principle that only super-specialists should prescribe super drugs.

In the course of my undergraduate medical education I spent a whole year on pharmacology and therapeutics. This is appropriate in so far as doctors are the only people licensed to prescribe many medications and therefore we, of all people, need to know about them. Drugs may have interactions with each other and they may have side effects. Indeed, it has been estimated that up to one in five of hospital admissions may be as a result of inappropriate prescription or unintentional side effects. I myself am a very reluctant prescriber. Also I tend to disbelieve a great deal of what I read about the actions and effectiveness of pharmaceutical substances. The pharmaceutical companies may be appropriately motivated by profit and I believe that they also have patients' welfare at heart – as do the doctors who prescribe the drugs. My scepticism is based upon my belief that we really know very little indeed about the workings of the human body and we are very often highly disrespectful of its ability to heal itself.

During the 20th century the pharmaceutical industry dramatically transformed the face of medical practice. General anaesthesia enabled a wide range of surgical procedures to be carried out. Antibiotics significantly reduced the incidence of infections and the damage that they caused, although improved housing conditions had an even greater effect. Replacement drugs such as insulin, thyroid hormone, cortisone and oestrogen vastly influenced patients' lives and dramatically changed the nature of the clinical problems seen most commonly on hospital wards. Many clinical conditions can nowadays be treated totally successfully with medication so that the patient should never get to the situation of requiring hospitalisation. The pharmaceutical industry, a favourite whipping boy, in fact deserves full credit for these amazing achievements in therapeutics. When people complain that drugs are over-prescribed, they should remember that the pharmaceutical industry researches them and produces them and markets them – all perfectly legitimate procedures in their business – but it is doctors who prescribe them.

The turf wars that are fought between consultant specialists in hospital are over the status of their individual departments. In simple terms their cry is "the illnesses that I look after are more important than yours". Cynically one might observe that the "most important" illnesses are those that tend to affect middle-class, middle-aged men – exactly the same sector of the population that provides most consultant specialists. It is true that this is a highly productive sector of the community but it does not necessarily follow that they are therefore the most deserving of medical care. I recall a lady gynaecologist once observing that a survey of the Internet revealed that there were ten times as many studies on cancer of the breast as there are on cancer of the ovary, an equally destructive clinical condition. Her conclusion was that breasts are more important than ovaries in the minds of the male doctors who were primarily responsible for those research projects.

The most revered of hospital specialists used to be the cardiologists and chest physicians in the days when rheumatic fever, chronic bronchitis, emphysema and tuberculosis were rife. Perhaps in order to protect their territory, consultant specialists in these disciplines now try to convince us that hypercholesterolaemia (raised blood fats) and asthma are the major problems of a new age. I am unconvinced. Raised blood fats come a poor third to genetics and cigarette smoking in the cause of heart disease – but doctors mostly cannot do anything about genetics and don't know what to do about cigarette smoking – so they make a great hullabaloo about cholesterol. In fact the issue of dietary cholesterol is more complex than it initially appears. A high cholesterol diet may not necessarily lead to high cholesterol levels in the blood. We are still eating the same quantity of animal fat as our forebears ate one hundred years ago. The epidemic of cardiovascular disease is therefore more likely to be linked to a low fibre diet: we now eat one hundred times as much refined sugar as was consumed at the beginning of the last century. The recently classified Syndrome X, which is a combination of coronary artery disease and diabetes, may well originate in a diet that is low in fibre and high in refined sugar.

Asthma is now the diagnosis of the day, if not of the hour, and GPs are accused of under-diagnosing it. I think it is possibly over-diagnosed: every child with a slight wheeze is diagnosed as being asthmatic and given a range of inhalers. I am not convinced that this is good clinical practice. Severe asthma is a terrible disease – watching someone in *status asthmaticus*, when he or she cannot get out of it – is a frightening experience for any medical student or doctor. But *status asthmaticus*, or even mild or moderate asthma are not the inevitable consequence of untreated occasional wheezes, particularly in the hay-fever season.

In fact the largest expenditure for any disease treated in the NHS is said to be on diabetes, which is at times a consequence of over-indulgence. However, this figure may overlook the fact that cigarette smoking is the greatest killer of all, and over-indulgence in alcohol results in one in five of all hospital beds being occupied by people with alcohol-related clinical conditions. One in two of all people seen in Accident and Emergency Departments are there as a result of problems relating to either alcohol or drugs. Faced with this massive destruction from the products of addiction to food, cigarettes, alcohol and recreational drugs, the medical profession tends to turn the other way and get on with treating "real" diseases. Doctors may be prepared to treat the consequences of addiction – they can be real enough – but tend to express little interest in the cause, often believing it to be poor up-bringing, deprived social circumstances, weak will or stupid experiment. A simple examination of the achievements of people who suffer from nicotine addiction, alcoholism, drug addiction or eating disorders will very quickly reveal that these patients are frequently very far from weak-willed or stupid.

However, just as soldiers are trained to fight the last war rather than the next, doctors tend to be trained to fight the medical conditions of thirty to fifty years ago rather than those of the present day. The prescription of Methadone for heroin addicts – there are now over a million prescriptions of Methadone written out each year in the UK – is not a treatment at all. It is a substitute addiction with many of the same risks of the heroin that it replaces (or more commonly supplements). In fact Methadone (the "treatment") now kills twice as many people as heroin addiction (the "illness"). This level of carnage would never be accepted for any other medical treatment. But doctors tend to be bored by addicts and see them as a nuisance rather than regard their appropriate treatment as a challenge to the basic concepts of illness and therapeutics in which we were trained.

When it comes to considering the potential benefits or risks of prescribing a particular treatment, doctors are on safer ground in pharmacology, particularly now that the side-effects and interactions of drugs are listed on computer packages so that warnings may come up with each prescription. However, doctors may still make the mistake of prescribing too frequently simply because they can. "Cook-book" medicine, prescribing a drug for each symptom, is generally frowned upon in Western society but is almost a professional virility symbol in some other countries. Even so, it does occur in the UK, both in general practice and in hospital.

As far as the issue of whether a resource should be given to one patient rather than another, this is a particular problem as far as the NHS is concerned. "Distributing resources according to need" is a hallowed tenet of the NHS and I believe it causes a lot of problems. I would rather distribute resources according to the capacity of the recipient to benefit from the expenditure of that resource – because otherwise the resource is wasted on one patient while others are deprived of possible benefit.

Consider the case of an elderly lady who has cancer of the breast, varicose veins and cataracts. The cancer may initially be thought to be the most important of the three clinical conditions but it may be slow-growing and she might live for years without having any great discomfort from it or need for any dramatic treatment. The varicose veins, if they are not causing ulceration of the skin of the ankles, might be treated perfectly well with elastic stockings, rather than with surgery. She might then be able to live perfectly comfortably with them. The cataracts, on the other hand, are a major issue. They significantly reduce the quality of her vision and therefore reduce many of her pleasures and they will also lead to a significant risk of her tripping on loose carpets, or on other things that she cannot see, and consequently falling down and breaking a hip. This could land her in hospital for months and may lead to her death, whereas the treatment of cataracts is a very simple and inexpensive surgical operation. In this case, consideration of the capacity of the recipient to benefit would focus the attention first of all on the cataracts whereas the general, undefined, concept of need might have put the cancer at the top of the list of priorities. Treating it would have been expensive and painful and would not necessarily achieve any great benefit - whereas other, younger patients with more aggressive cancers might benefit very considerably from early intervention.

The plain fact is that the NHS will always have competition for resources. No system of medical care anywhere in the world could deliver perfect results on such a nebulous concept as providing "health to the nation". Perceived needs will always outstrip resources. It is therefore up to doctors to establish clear priorities in the treatment of patients, not only in the doctor's own clinical field of expertise but overall. If we do not do this, then administrators and the Government will do it for us – and we shall have only ourselves to blame.

The miracles of modern scientific advances are indeed miraculous - but they are also initially exceedingly expensive. Patients become aware of them through the press and on the Internet and then may ask – or sometimes demand – that they should be given the opportunity of benefiting from the latest miracle cure. Having had raised expectations that the State will always provide, they become bitter and resentful when they discover that it does not. Perhaps there are insufficient funds or specialists or nurses, or maybe the press jumped the gun and the procedure in question was still at the research stage rather than delivery level. One way or another, neither the State nor the private sector could ever provide absolutely everything that everyone needs, let alone wants. There will always be rationing in the NHS and it will usually take the form of a queue. New "wonder drugs" come on the market all the time, and new therapeutic procedures are announced with bewildering frequency but resources will always lag behind. Doctors would do well to explain this principle to their patients as well as they can, rather than blame the Government for mismanaging resources.

The medical profession tends to unite on just one issue: blaming the Government for "under-funding" the NHS. Whether or not the accusation is justified, the fact remains that all doctors - state and private - could do a great deal more to reduce costs by examining our own clinical practices and, in particular, our principles of applied pharmacology and therapeutics. Furthermore, patients might well benefit. When doctors in Canada went on strike and withdrew their labour from the state medical service, there were indications that many patients did rather well without them.

Chapter Seven

Surgery

Your life in their hands was the title of a television series on major surgical procedures some years ago. It made gruesome television, which seemed to be rather popular, but it may also have given the impression that patients need not bother too much about being responsible for their own healthcare because surgeons can always put us right in the end.

Nothing could be further from the truth: surgery should be the absolute last resort whereas we should focus primarily upon helping patients to stay fit and avoid doing things that damage themselves. That is easier said than done – but there is no doubt that it is correct in its emphasis.

Consider the causal relationship between cigarette smoking and coronary artery disease. Cigarette smokers have a very high incidence of damage to their coronary arteries and ultimately this may be "treated" with coronary artery bypass surgery or even with a heart transplant. This may be clinically appropriate for an individual patient who will die without the treatment but it is absolutely categorically the wrong treatment epidemiologically. Arterial bypasses or cardiac transplants cannot ever be considered to be routine procedures. The primary emphasis should be on helping people to give up smoking. That would be a worthy expenditure of medical time whereas dramatic procedures in a surgical operating theatre have a lot in common with theatrical performances of another kind. My own book, *Fifteen reasons for continuing to smoke (or not)*,(PROMIS Book 200) looks at the issue of why people smoke in the first place – because these are the precise issues that they will need to tackle if they are to give up smoking for good. Dr Alan Carr's book on treating cigarette smokers with hypnotherapy is inevitably more popular than mine because it gives an easy answer and expects relatively little from the patients. Again patients may be given false security in believing that other people will always be on hand to "fix" them.

Surgeons tend to be the ultimate "fixers" because the unconscious patient, under general anaesthetic, really has absolutely no contribution to make to the procedure. The question that arises sometimes is whether or not the operation should ever be done in the first place. When I lost my own gall bladder to the surgeon's knife it was because the pain was so excruciating that I could not function at all while I still had it. Since losing it, I have had no symptoms whatever: the procedure was totally curative. That does not mean that all inflamed or stone-filled gall bladders should necessarily be removed. The mere presence of stones is not an indication for surgery. However, it may be considered to be so in the private sector and that is totally unacceptable. Also in the private sector, concern has been expressed over the high number of hysterectomies that are performed. Why would fee-paying patients have a greater need than their NHS counterparts for this particular operation? Similarly, in both state and private sectors there is an increasing number of Caesarean sections for childbirth. Are these really for the safety of mother and baby or are they more commonly primarily for the convenience of the obstetricians in the timing of deliveries? Surgeons of all kinds may do unnecessary operations on the pretext of patient need but in fact for private gain for themselves or for convenience.

Leaving that specific can of worms to one side, there is still an issue of unnecessary or inappropriate surgery even in the NHS. Surgeons like to do operations because surgery is what they are trained to do and because they genuinely believe they are helping. However, there are times when they definitely do too much.

The various surgical procedures designed to "help" patients with eating disorders – stomach-stapling, intestinal bypass or shortening, jaw-wiring, liposuction and lipectomies – are testament to the failure of other approaches rather than evidence of successful treatments in themselves. Surgeons are generally not well placed to treat psychological conditions. When one hears of them doing frontal lobotomies for depression, or stereotactic ablation (precisely directed destruction) of parts of the brain implicated in addictive tendencies, then our natural response should be to recoil in horror or disgust rather than to applaud the surgeon's technical skill.

Yet even in their own field, surgeons may be tempted to do too much simply because they know how to do it. An obvious example is in the field of cosmetic surgery. Are we to be shamed by the natural process of aging or by having the occasional blemish? Is it appropriate for surgeons to pander to the perspectives of the tabloid press in this respect? If we were to achieve perfection would we value it? Can a surgical procedure ever be a substitute for natural self-esteem built upon one's own values and behaviour? I wonder how often cosmetic surgeons consider these issues when they are performing surgical operations for which there is no significant medical – or even cosmetic – need.

Yet even general surgeons or, for example, those who specialise in eyes, ear, nose and throat or gynaecology may fall into the trap of doing too much. Last week I saw a patient whose right eye had collapsed irretrievably as a result of infection following surgery for a mild cataract. The level of impaired vision did not merit the potential risks of surgery. On the other hand, the greatest treatable cause of blindness in the world – trachoma infestation – is treated very successfully with surgery for the resulting corneal scarring. Should nasal polyps be excised when they most commonly recede on being treated with steroid nasal drops? Should deviated nasal septa be treated with sub-mucous resection and should sinuses be washed out? Are these operations ever really necessary? Should lipomata (fatty lumps) be removed at all, unless they are dramatically disfiguring, when it is known perfectly well that they never become malignant? Should cysts or fibroadenomata in the breast or fibroids in the uterus be removed simply because they are there and not because there is doubt about the diagnoses or because they are disfiguring or in some way causing significant symptoms or disturbance to function? Should bunions be operated upon simply because they are unattractive rather than because they cause symptoms?

These questions are important because they illustrate that there may be a symbiotic relationship between some patients and their surgeons: the one wants to be fixed and the other wants to fix, and they meet on common ground. Whether they *should* do so – in the private sector, let alone at the expense of the State – is another matter. Surgeons are not gods with magic wands. They are technicians with specific, trained skills. How we use these professionals and how they perceive our needs and respond to our requests is an individual matter on both sides – but it certainly does not help if either they or we consider them to be divine.

Chapter Eight

Psychiatry

Under the terms of the Mental Health Act, consultant psychiatrists (working together at the specific time with psychiatric social workers and GPs) are allowed to certify people insane and deprive them of their liberty. The various sections of the Mental Health Act determine the length of time of "help" or "incarceration" (depending upon viewpoint). As a rule of thumb, psychiatrists will tend to see the process as being helpful whereas psychiatric social workers might see it as incarceration. The GP sits in the middle, as always.

It is for this reason that the Mental Health Act deprives any one person or profession from having total power in this area. Furthermore, lawyers may launch appeals on behalf of the patient so that Mental Health tribunals can reassess the need for patients to be confined in hospital against their will. The limits on psychiatrists becoming gods in this respect are therefore carefully delineated. Even in hospitals for the criminally insane, the patients can only be confined to those establishments if they are being treated with the aim of the restoration of mental health.

It is right that patients who are mentally ill should be protected in this way. Too many abuses of custodial power have occurred in the past. At the beginning of the last century girls were sometimes sent to mental hospitals for becoming illegitimately pregnant. In more recent times the concept of "care in the community" has attempted to transfer patients from institutional care to the wider community where they can be supervised on an outpatient basis by hospital specialists, psychiatric social workers and GPs. Whether or not this change of emphasis has been successful in helping patients, while at the same time protecting the general public, continues to be a matter of debate. This debate tends to run along political lines according to whether one believes that mental health problems are primarily influenced by nature (genetics) or nurture (social and environmental factors). The probability is that both influences play a part – but that does not prevent viewpoints from becoming polarised along political lines. In general the right wing would prefer to see people locked up, whether they be either mad or bad or both, and the left wing would like to see changes in government and in society in the hope that mental illness could be prevented.

Paradoxically many psychiatrics who have left-wing inclinations find themselves in a right-wing job. Perhaps it is this dichotomy that results in NHS consultant psychiatrists being allowed to retire on full pension five years younger than other consultant specialists. Perhaps the battles within themselves are even more wearing than the battles they have with patients.

This internal psychological problem in the minds of psychiatrists may not be considered to be all that important to the rest of us until we consider the particular problem of schizophrenia. The delusion states of this clinical condition tend to bring the sufferers from it into considerable conflict with society at large, including the police and the medical profession itself. Furthermore, there are a large number of these patients: estimates vary – again according to political viewpoint – but it is generally thought that 1.4% of the population may have psychiatric problems of this nature. That is a huge number of people: 15 for each GP and 300 for each consultant psychiatrist. These patients can cause significant disturbance at times in a general medical practice but can absolutely dominate the work of consultant psychiatrists. It is small wonder that psychiatrists tend at times to put up emotional defences in order to protect themselves from this constant psychological battering. At times they also suffer physical battering – as commonly occurs to all staff in mental institutions. Questions arise, however, on cause and effect. Are the patients naturally violent or are they reacting to the treatment that they receive?

I have some personal experience that may give me a bias in answering these questions. Firstly I have run an addiction treatment centre for the last seventeen years. Surveys done by Professor Geoffrey Stephenson, Emeritus Professor of Psychology at the University of Kent at Canterbury, have shown that our patients have a higher level of psychiatric morbidity than the average inpatient in psychiatric hospitals. Thus we are looking after a particularly difficult and demanding population. However, the experience of looking after a total of over 3,000 inpatients has not been peppered with incidents of violence. Occasionally someone will kick or punch a nurse in the detoxification unit in which patients are supervised, where necessary, for the first day or two of their stay with us, but this happens once or twice a year, if that, rather than three or four times a day, or even more frequently, which I gather is common in other institutions.

I myself believe that the main reason that we have such a low incidence of violence at PROMIS is because we very rarely use drugs other than for a short course of detoxification, where necessary, over the first four or five days of treatment. We use a very brief course of neuroleptic drugs such as Stelazine for patients who are frankly psychotic – but we do not use tranquillisers, anti-depressants or sleeping tablets, and therefore our patients are alert to what is going on rather than drugged out of their minds. They are treated with respect and dignity and therefore tend to behave in like manner towards each other and towards the staff.

From that experience I would tend to favour treatment in the community wherever possible. On the other hand, I have had the personal experience of being hounded, if not actually stalked. A particular individual – who is not a patient of mine but who once attended a lecture that I gave on state and private healthcare – has peppered me with accusations that I was involved in the murder of his sister and his aunt by the KGB. This accusation has been repeated by him to Scotland Yard, the General Medical Council, the BMA, the FBI, the CIA, to my staff and family and it has been published by him on the Internet. Eventually I was able to discover the name of the consultant psychiatrist who was responsible for his care. I was told that the patient was "depressed". I would have imagined that paranoid schizophrenia was a more appropriate diagnosis but I am not able to challenge that because I do not even know the man beyond our frequent telephone calls.

Another complete stranger burnt my house to the ground. The police believe that he targeted the house rather than me and my wife-but the experience was upsetting for us, to say the least. Losing all our personal possessions, including pictures and other treasures from childhood, was a bitter blow. Evidently, the consultant psychiatrist who had responsibility for this arsonist also said the man was "depressed".

I am left wondering whether "depression" is now a politically correct diagnosis. My professional and personal experiences therefore leave me in two minds. I am aware that patients can react extremely well in supportive circumstances but I am also aware that some can be a danger to the public – and the assaults that I have suffered are minor in comparison with rape or murder or other assaults that some people have endured.

The Mental Health Act exists for a purpose – to protect both the individual sufferers and society at large – and it should be used for both these functions simultaneously. Achieving that is a major challenge for the NHS. Facilities may be poor and staff dispirited. Under such circumstances it is small wonder that the first line of clinical approach tends to be pharmaceutical.

In my view these patients who often present the greatest clinical challenges, and the doctors and staff who work with them, should be given the best facilities and greatest support rather than the worst, as is often the case. I am well aware of my immense privilege at PROMIS: my wife and I own the building and have redesigned it to suit our clinical needs. Our psychologist son, Robin, and I hire and fire the staff according to whether or not they prove their ability. We pay them well from the fees we set for patients. The three of us put our own practical and clinical ideas into practice. I must be one of the very few doctors in the entire country who can say any, let alone all, of this. Of course, I make it sound easier than it is. Other doctors are welcome to copy my example if they so wish but they will soon come up against the many and various challenges that Meg, Robin and I have to face. Even so, I acknowledge my privilege – and hence that of my patients – and I would wish other doctors and patients to have the same opportunities that I have been privileged to experience. In my view that prospect is unlikely to happen until the medical profession comes to value psychiatric services alongside the "elite" specialities, such as cardiology and neurology. To change the structure and function of psychiatric hospitals to an effective degree really requires a change of status of psychiatric patients and their doctors and other carers in the minds of the medical profession at large and in the Department of Health. If there are individual gods in the medical profession, I would nominate psychiatrists who do the best they possibly can in providing services to an exceedingly damaged and damaging population and often in wretched circumstances and unsupported by their professional colleagues. Hell on earth knows few such equivalents in medical practice.

That being said, I do have to express concern over some basic aspects of psychiatric diagnosis and treatment. As a general practitioner, I see patients – or at any rate those who come to see doctors at all – as they really are. Psychiatrists in the UK generally see only those patients who are referred to them by GPs or by other specialists. They may therefore get a distorted picture of what most human beings are really like. Working with mentally disturbed people every day inevitably causes a level of vicarious traumatisation. Doctors who work in infectious fever units are not the only ones who "catch" things from their patients. I have acknowledged that psychiatrists have an extremely demanding professional life but I believe that this sometimes leads them to treat first and diagnose afterwards. The most obvious example of this is in the use of neuroleptic drugs (anti-psychotics) and mood-altering medications such as tranquillisers, anti-depressants and sleeping tablets. I recall a consultant psychiatrist telling me in my medical student years that he gave patients barbiturates to help patients to get to sleep and amphetamines to help them wake up in the morning and that he did so secure in the knowledge that these drugs are not addictive. As little as ten years ago doctors were saying the same about tranquillisers – and that misconception has also now largely been laid to rest alongside those concerning barbiturates and amphetamines.

However, anti-depressants, particularly the selective serotonin re-uptake inhibitors (SSRIs) such as Prozac, Seroxat, Lustral and Efexor are the wonder drugs of the moment. They are prescribed both in general practice and in hospital with alarming frequency. We are told in medical journals that if the first anti-depressant is ineffective in helping the patient's symptoms, we should try a second – or even a third or fourth. Thus doctors have become wedded to pharmacology and they adjust their diagnoses to justify the treatment that they have already decided to give. On this basis the diagnosis "clinical depression" (which has no specific clinical basis whatever) now serves to provide absolute justification for the prescription of any anti-depressant. "Agitated depression" justifies the prescription of both an anti-depressant and a tranquilliser. "Psychotic depression" justifies the prescription of a neuroleptic drug as well as an anti-depressant. These diagnoses are all clinical fictions: they exist in the minds of the doctors rather than those of the patients.

To be sure, acute psychosis exists: I have seen it frequently in my work in general practice and even more frequently when it is drug-induced in patients whom I see at our addiction treatment centre. These patients may sometimes need anti-psychotic medication on a short-term basis for a few days. The risks of the long-term use of anti-psychotic medication, however, are very considerable. Doctors who prescribe these drugs may at times be unaware that the disturbances they see in the behaviour of patients on long-term medication may actually be caused by the drugs themselves rather than be part of the patient's underlying clinical condition. Neuroleptic (anti-psychotic) drugs appear to "work" on a long-term basis by causing physical damage to the brain, such as seen in tardive dyskinesia, a progressive disorder of movement and co-ordination. I can think of no circumstances whatever in which that could be clinically or ethically appropriate.

To prescribe drugs for patients suffering from "depression" is, in my view, very rarely justifiable – if ever. If patients were to say that they were "sad" or "unhappy" rather than "depressed", then perhaps doctors would be less tempted to write a prescription for an anti-depressant, followed by a diagnosis of "depression". However, I do not blame the patients for this clinical disaster: only doctors are responsible for the prescriptions that are written and subsequently taken. Furthermore, anti-depressants do not necessarily clear the mind to make it more capable of resolving problems, nor reduce the risk of suicide. Patients often use an overdose of anti-depressants to kill themselves.

Forty million prescriptions for anti-depressants, tranquillisers and sleeping tablets are now written each year in the UK. This is an appalling indictment of the medical profession in general practice and in hospital. That number of people cannot possibly need pharmaceutical drugs. The human brain is the most delicate and sensitive organ that we possess and we should treat it with respect. We know virtually nothing about brain biochemistry. We may baffle each other and our patients with complex diagrams and formulae illustrating neurotransmission pathways – but this is a drop in an ocean of undiscovered knowledge on how the brain works. Furthermore, the brain mostly looks after itself very well and has the capacity to heal its function when it is treated respectfully by the patients themselves (in sorting out their personal philosophies and not taking damaging "recreational" substances) and doctors (in not reaching automatically for a prescription). The human brain should be viewed with awe and wonder. To do anything less is to usurp the power of whatever "God" created it.

Chapter Nine

Health Centres

I created the first NHS group general medical practice in the area in which I work in South Kensington in central London so I have considerable first-hand knowledge on this subject. In those days I believed in group practice. I believed that a group of doctors working together could provide a range of services and expertise that no individual doctor could provide. By using our full allowance of two staff per doctor (although the Government paid only 70% of their salaries and we had to provide the balance from our own remuneration) we were able to employ six staff as receptionists, secretaries or nurses. We were not allowed to employ physiotherapists or counsellors and we were not allowed to have our own x-ray unit or pathology laboratory on the premises. The waiting room had to be a certain size, according to Government specification. On this particular issue I pointed out that the need for seats in a waiting room depended upon the length of consulting hours and the proper management of an appointment system. Those were novel ideas in those days and they were not acceptable – so we were not given the full allowance for our premises.

I also pointed out that there are no "green field" sites in central London and therefore one has to modify existing buildings as best one can to suit the needs of general medical practice. Again, the NHS bureaucrats were unimpressed and said that regulations were regulations. Also in those days there were no special payments for taking on new patients – who inevitably require more work because of the need to get to know them. In South Kensington where the local population likely to use the NHS mostly lives in bed-sits or multi-occupation flats, the turnover of our patients was close to 100% in four years.

Relationships with local hospitals were not conducive to a good standard of clinical care in general practice. During my time in the group practice, we did three surveys:

i First, I looked at the use of hospital diagnostic facilities by the 120 general practitioners in the local area. The results showed that the average GP did one pathology test of any kind (blood tests, urine tests, swabs and so on) per day, one x-ray of any kind a week and one cardiograph a month. Bearing in mind that in those days each GP had an average of 2,200 NHS patients, this was evidence of clinical neglect on a simply massive scale. Diagnosis was little more than guesswork. Certainly the hospitals did nothing to encourage improvements of clinical standards in general practice. To obtain a full blood count, anterior/posterior and lateral chest x-rays and a cardiograph, I would have to send the patient to three different hospitals. Each would provide one of the services but not the others. The local teaching hospital offered no facilities at all to GPs. The dean of that teaching hospital had been known to tear up GPs' letters unopened in the presence of medical students and the patient in order to demonstrate that they were not worth reading. In the absence of available diagnostic facilities, what else could the doctors write other than "Dear Specialist, please see this patient."? However, my own survey largely proved his point. At the same time, the dean of another teaching hospital said that he would not offer a place at his (note the pronoun) medical school to someone wanting to do general practice – because it was a waste of a place. It was Lord Moran, Winston Churchill's doctor, who said that GPs were the failures of the medical profession: they fell off the ladder. With attitudes like that, it is small wonder that hospitals generally ignored their GP colleagues and that GPs gave up trying to be clinicians.

ii. The second survey was in the delays in GPs receiving correspondence from the hospital concerning their patients who had recently been admitted. Bearing in mind that hospitals would not see patients for GPs without having a letter from the GP in hand or even in advance, the figures revealed in the survey make disturbing reading. The discharge "chit", simply saying that the patient had been in hospital, arrived on average ten days after the patient left one or other of the eighteen hospitals covered in the survey, and was only received at all for 60% of the patients. The full discharge summary arrived on average six weeks after the patient had left hospital; with the star prize going to one that arrived after nine months. (Subsequent to the publication of the survey we received one that was written two years after the patient left hospital.) Again this was evidence of the disdain with which hospital doctors treated their GP colleagues, although it has to be said that it also reflected the paucity of secretarial services in hospitals. When we published the survey in *The Times* newspaper correspondence columns, we looked for ways in which the situation could be improved. A number of doctors complained to me that we had "washed professional dirty linen in public". I felt that it was precisely the right place for it to be washed: patients deserved to know just how poor the service was in the NHS, despite the repeated claims from the Government that it was "the envy of the world".

iii. The third survey was on the number of staff employed by local GPs. The results were that altogether there was one full-time member of staff to every five GPs and one part-time member of staff to every three. Bearing in mind that a large number of GPs in the area were single-handed, it can be seen that a significant proportion of the GPs had no staff whatever, not even a receptionist to turn on the light, and certainly no secretary to type the records or nurse to do the various things that are helpful in their own right as well as relieving the pressure on the doctor's time. Again, it was the patients who suffered.

Doctors' remuneration at that time was primarily on a capitation fee basis. We were paid according to the total number of patients rather than on the work that we actually did. There were some "items of service" payments but very few. Generally there was very little to be gained financially by doing better quality of work and a great deal to be gained by spending less on premises and staff and equipment of any kind. A further factor is that, particularly in our area, there were very few district nurses, social workers and health visitors employed by the Local Health Authority and none at that time were seconded to GPs. Eventually, largely as a result of pressure from the Royal College of General Practitioners, the clinical environment of general medical practice gradually improved. However, there still remains a very great deal to be done in city centres where the cost of staff and premises are particularly high. Here the Local Health Authorities tend to provide one or two "show piece" health centres and ignore the rest. But the rest cannot be ignored: the majority of the population lives in cities. Anyone can run a general medical practice in rural Oxfordshire or Devon but the real challenges come in London, Birmingham, Manchester, Sheffield, Cardiff, Swansea, Edinburgh, Glasgow, Belfast and so on. Take away the major cities and there really is very little left for the NHS to do. Yet the Government tends to trumpet the achievements of general practice in geographical areas where the challenges simply bear no comparison with those of city centres. In my view, NHS general practice works in city centres or it does not work at all.

My two partners and I tried to do our bit for England in our group practice but, despite all the advantages of choosing our own premises, colleagues, staff and management systems, it still did not really work. Instead of benefiting from each other's personal and clinical support, we found that on many issues we achieved the lowest common denominator. The practice moved forward at the pace of the slowest member on each issue. We could have survived that but we could not survive the incoming Labour Government and Harold Wilson's "social contract" between the Government and all "useful" people. Clearly he did not consider GPs to be among the "useful" members of the community because our income was increased by 6% whereas our wages bill and other expenses went up by 30%. We already spent 40% of our gross income on the practice, even after the reimbursement of expenses. The practice would obviously go broke unless we made immediate significant changes. We divided according to the ages of our children. Mine were already at boarding school and therefore it did not matter too much if I took on private work in the evenings or weekends in order to maintain the standard of service to my NHS patients. I had never previously taken private work and I did not want to do so then but I was not prepared to compromise on the standard of service that I was then giving to my NHS patients. My partners, with young children, understandably made the opposite decision, to cut the services in order to protect personal time with family. Sadly for all of us, the partnership dissolved and I moved next door to return to single-handed practice.

Into these new premises I installed a simple x-ray unit and pathology laboratory and also employed my wife as a physiotherapist. None of these services were reimbursable by the NHS but I refused to provide a different quality of care to my NHS and private patients. The NHS, however, has a further complication in the system of reimbursement of staff salaries and the costs of premises: the proportion of private practice results in that same level of deduction of the reimbursements. I spent four years trying to persuade the Department of Health to adopt the design of my medical practice, with its own diagnostic facilities, as an alternative to standard health centres but I completely failed. At the end of that time I was actually spending more on my NHS patients than I was earning from the NHS for their care. I therefore resigned – and, interestingly, received quite a lot of abuse from some of my former patients for "depriving them of NHS facilities". It would have been invidious to explain that the facilities were in fact mine and that I had given the use of them free of charge. In any case I had more important – and more dignified – battles to fight. This story illustrates a major disturbing feature in the management of the NHS, or perhaps any state-funded bureaucracy, the penalties of innovation. I don't suppose this will ever change.

In a state system, ideas come from the centre and are imposed upon the periphery. That is exactly what happened with health centres. The Department of Health, in its wisdom and on the advice of their own "committee doctors", many of whom had previously failed to survive in clinical practice, sees general medical practice as having primarily a social function. Such clinical function as is acknowledged is seen mostly in the care of minor illnesses (so that patients do not trouble the more important doctors in hospital) and in the sorting-office function of knowing which specialists would be best placed to deal with each clinical condition. I suspect that hospital doctors themselves may have influenced the Department of Health in this respect, just as they influence the medical insurance companies to restrict reimbursement of fees to their own consultant colleagues rather than also include GPs.

Be that as it may, the Department of Health, perhaps in consultation with corresponding "committee doctors" from the BMA or Royal College of General Practitioners, hit upon the idea of health centres. In these palaces, GPs would work alongside nurses and health visitors and social workers and chiropodists and sometimes dentists and Uncle Tom Cobley and all. Strangely, they usually left out x-ray units and pathology laboratories. The idea was to provide a "one-stop shop" but this was seen more in social terms than clinical. I suppose the philosophical concept behind this is that patients will not get seriously ill in the first place if the nanny state caters for all the minor ups and downs of their personal and social lives. I can see that argument myself in my emphasis on the importance of general practitioners developing counselling skills in order to deal with the emotional crises of patients' lives before they go on to get physical consequences of one kind or another. However, I can also see the incredible waste of time and money in focusing the attention of expensively trained doctors on social and other aspects of their patients' lives when these matters are better dealt with by other professionals. My own preference would be for doctors to leave health centres altogether and work in primary care units that are equipped with diagnostic facilities to enable them to make early diagnosis of significant disease: to my mind the most important of all clinical functions in general medical practice.

At present, nurses in general practice largely do work that could be done by care assistants, GPs do work that could be done by nurse practitioners and then hospital specialists do the work that could have been done by GPs. The economic and clinical consequences of this mismanagement of resources are absolutely vast.

I am not sure that health centres would lose anything from their current clinical and social functions if they were to be deprived of doctors working on the premises. Social workers can still do whatever it is that social workers do and the district nurses, health visitors and all the rest would probably enjoy the opportunities provided by greater autonomy. It has been argued before that there is no reason why doctors should necessarily consider themselves to be the head of a clinical team in a health centre. I am simply taking that argument one step further and saying that there is no reason why they should be there at all. I don't see them as gods – but I do believe that five or six years of medical training should be put to better use than they are now.
The present Government is currently looking at this same issue in a rather different way, hoping to encourage more GPs to increase their specialist skills, such as in

minor surgery, so that they can take on more clinical work in the community and relieve the hard-pressed hospitals, particularly in their outpatient clinics and Accident and Emergency Departments. Obviously I can see the advantages of this proposal but I can also see four disadvantages:

i. Hospitals should sort themselves out and become better organised rather than expect GPs to bail them out of their difficulties.
ii. The real need in general practice is for diagnostic facilities rather than for treatment facilities. The cart is being put before the horse.
iii. Single-handed medical practice, for me the essence of personal commitment to patients, is being progressively devalued.
iv. General practice is a discipline in its own right rather than an offshoot of hospitals. GPs have long-term perspectives on their patients' lives. To lose this interest in people and substitute an obsession with diseases would be to put the clock back, continuing the perspectives of medical schools, as opposed to those that we develop from clinical experience of working in the community. At medical school we were taught about diseases but we had no insight into who might get them and why in a particular social setting. In this respect we had absolutely no understanding of the most important clinical function of all: prevention.

Prevention is not simply a question of infant inoculations and cervical smear tests. It has far more to do with the development of appropriate counselling skills in order to help patients to express their concerns before they damage themselves in one way or another. In medical school we were given absolutely no training whatever in counselling skills – which seems quite extraordinary to me today from the perspective of a lifetime in general practice, where 30% of the consultations have a significant emotional content and all consultations have an emotional element to some extent. I suppose the only "counselling" we learnt in medical school was to say, "don't smoke" and "cut down on the booze". Obviously these are important injunctions but it is hardly the epitome of counselling skills. On these particular issues, the process of helping people to give up smoking is very challenging indeed and goes way beyond telling people all the dreadful medical things that will happen to them if they continue to smoke. Equally, I believe that the counselling skills involved in helping people to give up alcohol or drugs or deal with eating disorders or come to terms with bereavement or other grief processes or unemployment are a fundamentally necessary part of the skills of a fully competent general practitioner.

We are not gods in this respect – and should never be seen as such simply because we work in the emotional field, helping patients with aspects of their lives that really matter to them – but we could be a lot better trained than we generally are. Furthermore, if we become skilled in the work that patients actually bring to us, rather than exclusively in what we were trained to do in medical school, we would be excited rather than disappointed when we see patients who suffer from emotional rather than physical problems. The concept of "heart-sink" patients should have absolutely no place in general practice. These, among others, are the patients we are there to help.

Chapter Ten

Counselling

Whenever there is a disaster they send in the counsellors. We don't seem to be able to manage without them. There are now more counsellors in the UK than there are doctors. I am somewhat ambivalent about this because there are times when I wonder how helpful they really are. In my general medical practice I do all the counselling myself but in the inpatient PROMIS Recovery Centre in Kent, we employ eight full-time counsellors and in the outpatient PROMIS Counselling Centre in London we employ a further six. I therefore very much believe in the potential effectiveness of counselling work. However, in the course of my own counsellor training – that I instigated myself after leaving medical school – and in the course of my work in the specialist field of addiction, I have generally been rather unimpressed with the training of counsellors and with their clinical skills. Obviously I know counsellors who have had excellent training and who have considerable skills, but the overall impression that I have is of the curate's egg.

The British Association of Counselling and Psychotherapy is very much aware of the shortcomings in its field and is keen to develop a compulsory registration system that will monitor the training of counsellors before they are able to offer their services to the general public. At present, believe it or not, if someone decides to be a counsellor, there is nothing whatever that can stop him or her from doing so or even from saying that he or she has a special interest in childhood sexual abuse or bereavement or whatever. This state of affairs is obviously untenable. On the other hand, I was unimpressed, to say the least, with members of another counselling organisation who were so wedded to politically correct ideas of positive discrimination in staffing that I found their approach to me, with a request that I should register with them, exasperating. As it happens my accountants are Indians, one of my radiographers is Chinese, the previous head of our outpatient unit is gay and we recruited a young woman on to our management staff fully knowing that she had cancer of the breast. She gave us excellent service for the eighteen months before she died.

I mention these particular staff members in order to make the point that I have absolutely no interest whatever in people's racial origin, sexual orientation or disabilities: I employ people on one principle only: talent. I am not an employment agency: I take on staff for positions of considerable responsibility in the treatment of patients and I am proud of being ruthless in hiring those who show promise and firing those who do not deliver. In this way we have built up a loyal staff who respect each other because they know that they have all gone through the same rigorous selection and retention process. Having a stable staff is immensely important. In The PROMIS Unit, my medical practice, the staff have been with me for many years and this makes an enormous difference to the atmosphere of the Unit. We know each other well and rely upon each other. I pay the wages but they really run the place. This enables me to focus upon my clinical work and leave most administrative issues to them. In my addiction work, the counselling staff are selected almost exclusively from former patients. "Poacher turned gamekeeper" is an extremely valuable principle in addiction work. Patients very soon discover that it is impossible to bullshit someone who has done it all before. They may try but they don't get very far. We are very dependent upon the counsellors' insights and clinical skills in this respect and in many others.

One thing that concerns me very considerably, not only in the field of addiction but also generally, is that the principle of "poacher turned gamekeeper" may be thought to be sufficient in itself. It is not. Historically that may be a preferable starting position – the concept of "the wounded healer" probably originated in classical times – but professional training begins rather than ends at that point. I was concerned to discover that a number of nationally-known organisations have very little training – beyond an initiation period of sorts – for their counselling staff. For one very well-known charitable organisation the total training time is 36 hours. That is frankly appalling; but a quick check with organisations that purport to help people with marital difficulties, bereavement, indebtedness, childhood abuse or abandonment or other forms of emotional trauma will reveal the general extraordinary lack of training of any stature for the counsellors employed. Perhaps only the Samaritans can afford to have minimal training. Their personal experience really does give them particular insights.

I do not believe that doctors or psychologists are automatically trained to be counsellors simply as a result of their professional training. I myself had no counselling training whatever in three years of university and another three years of medical school. I was let loose on the general public in the emotional mêlée of general practice with absolutely no training on how to deal with human beings. All I knew was how to deal with their diseases. I discovered very quickly that I needed further training – and to this day I still believe that I need further training. So far I have spent eighteen months of day-release training with the Lincoln Centre staff from the Tavistock Clinic, learning about analytical psychotherapeutic approaches, several weekend courses on Transactional Analysis and Gestalt at Metanoia, two separate weeks of training in Reality Therapy and Choice Theory, six visits to the USA training in psychodrama, and I have completed both the level 1 and the level 2 training courses in Eye Movement Desensitisation and Reprocessing (EMDR), a particularly successful procedure in the treatment of post-traumatic stress disorder but also helpful in other psychological problems. The most refreshing aspect of EMDR is that it accelerates the therapeutic learning process in patients. This is a far cry from therapies that require years on a couch or hour after hour of deep and meaningful discussion. In my professional counselling work I have had continuing supervision first by a clinical psychologist, later by a Jungian psychotherapist, then by a psychodramatist and now by a clinical psychologist specialising in EMDR. I would like to have even more training in caring for the psychological aspects of patients' illnesses and I get some new insights every year on the week-long conferences that I attend twice a year in the USA. I find these conferences and the supervision sessions to be vital to the maintenance and improvement of my counselling skills, such as they are.

As far as our own counselling staff are concerned, we give them a one-year training towards a diploma in addiction counselling, registered previously with the Associated Examining Board and now with the Federation of Drug and Alcohol Professionals, and that counts as the first year of a three-year training course towards an MSc in addiction counselling run jointly by PROMIS and the University of

Greenwich. Our training courses are headed by Professor Geoffrey Stephenson, Emeritus professor of psychology at the University of Kent at Canterbury, and two full-time members of our staff have PhDs in psychology. Another three members of our part-time staff are similarly qualified. I believe that our counsellor trainees are given training and experience second to none. Even so, we are very much aware that we can never actually teach anybody anything: all we can do is to encourage our trainees to learn. Additionally, and most importantly, our own trainees (as opposed to those from elsewhere: twenty five this year) are in full-time placement with us, gaining their clinical experience every day and learning professional skills from our senior staff. The one day a week allocated solely to training, either in our own counselling premises in London or at the University of Greenwich, is a significant commitment from PROMIS to its counselling staff but we believe that it is not only appropriate but vitally necessary. Furthermore, we do not necessarily retain on our staff those trainees who may have passed the first-year diploma course but whom we do not feel have developed sufficient practical skills in the day-to-day work of the Recovery Centre or Counselling Centre. Why should we accept anything less? Why should anyone else? How can anyone else?

My wife, Meg, who supervises our family programmes for the Recovery Centre, trained initially as a physiotherapist and then as a Montessori schoolteacher and she followed this with a Bachelor of Education degree in London University. Then she trained as a laboratory scientist in order to help me in the medical practice and then as a Rogerian person-centred counsellor in order to prepare herself for work at the Recovery Centre and Counselling Centre. Like me, she also has regular on-going supervision. I have to say, in parenthesis, that she has finally put her foot down – saying that she is not prepared to take on further training courses simply to satisfy my professional changes of direction! In fact I have no intention of making any further changes: I have no ambition whatever other than to continue my work in general medical practice and as a counsellor.

I tend to be faintly amused when people call themselves therapists or psychotherapists but I suppose I speak from the privileged position of being an established doctor in the first place. If I had no other qualification then perhaps I would want some form of title to reflect my training and experience. However, the use of the titles "therapist" or "psychotherapist" by counsellors I have met seems to bear absolutely no relationship to their training and experience. The title is often simply a "handle" to impress patients – and possibly charge higher fees – and to my mind that shows a dangerous lack of humility.

Counselling involves a great deal more then nodding the head and smiling. Groucho Marx established that process as his favourite convention when playing contract bridge and I agree with him: it works very well. However, counselling skills must surely involve a very great deal more than that. Counsellors need to be able to speak and observe at the same time, to hear what is not being said as well as what is actually said, to observe body language and the emotional nuances of inter-personal interactions – and, all at the same time, actually bring some coherence and insight to the overall process. Ultimately the intention of counselling is to help the patient to move forward and to function more effectively. To be able to do all these things at the same time is a considerable challenge.

At PROMIS we therefore discourage our trainees from making any spoken contribution to the group therapy sessions in the first two or three months of their employment. Immediately a group therapy session is over we take them to the staff room and get them to tell us what they saw and heard. They quickly become aware of what they missed as a result of focusing upon the speaker at any one time rather than on the effect that his or her words were having on the rest of the group or on what the others were doing while the speaker was holding forth. They would never have been able to observe all this if they had been concentrating on preparing their own contribution to the therapy session. In due course, with a senior counsellor to supervise them, we allow them to run the simple groups such as hearing a patient expound his or her "life-story" or do a "Step I" group in which a patient recounts his or her experience of powerlessness and unmanageability in the use of alcohol, drugs, food or other addictive substances and processes. From that they gradually move on to assisting in the "process groups" when anything can happen. Some of our staff, in addition to the training that they receive at PROMIS, also do additional training of their own choosing elsewhere, such as I did myself.

One staff member has developed a particular interest in Transactional Analysis and another two are following me in my interest in psychodrama. Three of the staff joined me in the EMDR training. Training and supervision are on-going processes rather than one-off experiences after which one can sit back and relax, confident that one "knows" something.

At PROMIS we do not generally do one-to-one counselling because we believe - from considerable experience - that any addict can always outwit an individual counsellor. We need the support of the other patients in the therapeutic group. We also need the support and insight and observational capacity of other counsellors. We therefore very rarely run group therapy sessions on our own and we always discuss any group therapy session with the other counselling staff afterwards. We work as a group of counsellors helping a group of patients and we prepare them for group interdependence in Alcoholics Anonymous and other Anonymous Fellowships.

There is a place for one-to-one counselling in intervention and in aftercare, following discharge from primary treatment in either the PROMIS Recovery Centre or the full-time treatment course in the PROMIS Counselling Centre. We do some of this work ourselves but mostly we refer to other counsellors whom we respect for their particular experience in our specific professional field. The reason that we tend not to do this work ourselves, as a general principle, is that we do not wish patients to form dependent relationships with us or us with them. We are catalysts, taking part in the reaction but then coming out and being ready to start again with someone else. The problem of dependency upon individual counsellors can be very considerable. I recall one starry-eyed patient describing a particular counsellor as "a healer". I was highly unimpressed. At the end of any group therapy session patients should be talking to each other rather than to the staff and at the end of their time in treatment they should be thanking each other rather than the staff.

This self-negation is very difficult for trainees at first but it is a basic belief of our work with addicts that our responsibility as counsellors is to show them what we do in our own continuing recovery from addiction but not do their work for them. The same principle applies to bringing up children beyond their very early years so our counsellors may well benefit from our training when they come to apply at home the principles that they have learnt in their professional lives. Nonetheless, in general, it is vitally important that the two areas of home and work should be kept totally separate. At the end of the working day I go home and I leave the concerns for my patients behind me. Obviously there are some occasions when this is impossible; I defy anyone to be unaffected by stories of child abuse or rape – and if they are unaffected then they should certainly not work in the counselling field – but even then I have to let it go after a time of reflection so that I can get on with my personal life.

Even so, these stories should not result in rendering us incapable of doing our work dispassionately. I may feel, and I am perfectly happy to show my feelings, but that does not throw me off course. When counsellors' personal lives become enmeshed with their professional lives, they burn out. They may want to blame their employing institution but the real problem is in themselves in failing to establish appropriate boundaries. Compulsive helpers, who use themselves as if they were drugs to help other people, need to address these issues long before they begin counsellor training. Even when they have completed their counsellor training in our particular field, they should work mostly with family members rather than with the primary addicts who are addicted to mood-altering substances and processes. In other words they should employ their insights into compulsive helping by working with other people who may have a similar problem. Primary addicts would generally eat them alive.

One way or another, my work as a counsellor has been the most challenging work that I have ever done. I have been a junior hospital doctor on a cardiology ward so I know about the sharp end of clinical practice. I have been an officer cadet in the Royal Signals in the days of National Service, before I ever thought of being a doctor, so I know about physical stamina, not only on the drill square but also for days and nights on end in the winter on the North Yorkshire moors. I have been a pupil in a British private school. I know about stress.

Counselling, however, demands emotional stamina at the same time as intellectual understanding and interpersonal skills. Dealing with thoughts, feelings and behaviour all at the same time is extremely demanding – which is precisely why we guard our training programmes so jealously at PROMIS. It also explains why, when I hear on television that after some major incident they have sent in the "counsellors", my response tends to be "Oh God".

Chapter Eleven

"Alternative" Medicine

As I have said, I am a very reluctant prescriber. In general I do not like prescribing pharmaceutical drugs unless they are absolutely necessary. The body and the mind look after themselves well enough for most of the time. The major improvements in healthcare over the centuries have been due far more to purity of water supply, proper sanitation, warm housing and an improved diet rather than anything that the medical profession has done.

The birth of scientific medicine was really only about one hundred years ago. Prior to that doctors sensibly advised fresh air and healthy diet but were powerless to do much more than that. When they did take action – such as therapeutic bleeding – the results were often disastrous, even when the patient was the monarch. Patients were often justifiably frightened of their doctors but felt that they had little alternative choice.

This fear of the medical profession has carried over into today and is still justified to some extent. Doctors still fill graveyards with our mistakes, sometimes acknowledging them but perhaps, more frequently, not even being aware of them. We may completely miss a diagnosis or we may provide an inappropriate treatment. We try to do otherwise but inevitably mistakes occur and our patients suffer.

The blossoming of "alternative" remedies in recent years is partly due to the understandable fear of placing oneself at the mercy of the medical profession but it is also part of an "alternative" political and social scene, populated in part by "the worried well". Brown rice, muesli, obsessively militant feminism, the peace movement and a reluctance to take antibiotics sometimes seem to go together as a political package, rather than as the product of individual thought. Interestingly, stopping smoking does not appear to be an important part of this philosophical ragbag. There are similar clusters at the opposite end of the political spectrum. Perhaps one such cluster would be paternalism, fox hunting, fine wines and cigars, red meat and a predisposition to gout. The former cluster may have come about partly in rebellion against the latter cluster, which had been the dominant culture in earlier years. Multinationalism – global capitalism – is the current divisive force. Some believe it to be a virtue and cannot wait to the see world rid itself of socialism and religion. Others see it as a vice and cannot wait for a multicultural Utopia where there shall be no more war and no more profit and with people smiling benignly upon each other, not necessarily under the influence of cannabis that has been genetically modified to improve its potency.

"Alternative" medicine is essentially a political concept for the most part, not dividing so much along party political lines, but more the province of liberals, uniting those who are warm in heart but perhaps at times a bit soft in the head. That being said, it has to be acknowledged that a significant number of doctors employ "alternative" concepts and practices alongside their traditional medical approaches. Many will share my own reluctance to prescribe pharmaceutical substances. Others will be aware that "scientific" medicine does not have all the answers.

Scientific medicine was meant to dispose of witchcraft, shamanism and various other forms of hocus pocus and mumbo jumbo but it has not succeeded. The fault lies largely in our educational system right from the start in primary schools. Global warming, deforestation, pollution and the general destruction of the environment are concepts that are deemed appropriate for young minds, even when there is little or no supporting scientific evidence. By contrast, metamorphosis, the development of frogs from tadpoles or butterflies from caterpillars, is about the limit of reliable science taught in primary schools. Truly useful subjects, such as learning the difference between myth and reality are ignored altogether.

From that starting position it is hardly surprising that adults find scientific medicine mysterious and frightening. However much the television soap operas include public health messages in their story lines, and whatever the impressively high viewing figures for the television programme ER, set in a hospital Accident and Emergency department, the public remain generally remarkably ignorant of the scientific world in general and scientific medicine in particular. A television advert claims that a particular product will "kill 99% of all household germs", but even in elementary science lessons one learns that the remaining 1% could cause havoc the very next day because of the rate at which they reproduce, particularly in an environment where there is no longer any competition from other microbes. These fundamental flaws in scientific understanding in our culture are not trivial: they illustrate a profound ignorance of matters that can be important in people's daily lives. The tabloid press and the increasingly dumbed-down television stations serve our society poorly. There is perhaps some hope for salvation through the Internet – or at least through that small part of it that is not occupied by pornography.

The "alternative" scene is unscientific – and that is often paraded as a badge of honour! Physical concepts that are just plain wrong are sometimes believed with a fervour worthy of religious fundamentalists. Homeopathy, using substances in vanishingly small dilutions, and expounding philosophical concepts of treating like with like, have no scientific evidence to support them. I am all in favour of people avoiding pharmaceutical substances altogether if possible – but why take anything at all? Is not the concept of "a pill for every ill" just as dangerous and debilitating when the pill contains nothing more active than cotton wool? Osteopaths and chiropractors do wonderful things with their hands when they manipulate people to reduce pain but their mouths tend to do dreadful things to the science that underlies orthopaedics and rheumatology. It seems obligatory to these alternative therapists that spinal discs should be displaced, one leg be shorter than the other and muscles should be full of fibrous knots.

My concern is not simply that these fictions are spoken but rather that they are heard and believed. Are patients really so obsessed with the need to know why they are in pain that they will be gullible enough to believe this claptrap? Surely it would be more sensible to go to a doctor to get an appropriate diagnosis, ruling out conditions that require urgent intervention by one branch or another of the medical profession, and then go to the osteopath or chiropractor for pain relief that avoids the use of pharmaceutical substances. When it comes to radionics, Reiki, Bach flowers and Chinese herbal remedies, the less said the better – except that Chinese herbal remedies can sometimes cause actual harm.

Patients get better when they believe they will do so. This is known as the placebo effect and it is a very real and important scientific observation. We may not understand precisely how placebos work but there is no doubt that the mind significantly influences the body. Nor is there any doubt that some people seem to have the ability to harness the placebo effect therapeutically in the treatment of patients. I see nothing odd in that. I do not believe that our current understanding of scientific principles is absolute: there is vastly more to learn. I anticipate that some of the things that we will discover in the future would look preposterous to us today – but that has been true of all scientific advances throughout history.

Recently I was fascinated by a television report on monkeys who had been trained to use a joystick to change the position of coloured circles on a television screen. They learned to focus upon the screen and move the coloured circles in particular ways in order to achieve particular end results. The joystick was then disconnected from the computer producing the images on the screen – but the monkeys still moved the coloured circles as before! People to whom I have mentioned this experiment have described it as "spooky". I personally find it absolutely fascinating, perhaps illustrating telepathic powers that we ourselves may have but which we have forgotten because the capacity for speech means that we no longer rely upon them. Yet how wonderful it would be if we could reawaken those powers.

In other words, my mind is not at all closed to the limitations of our current understanding of science: I rejoice in it because of the possibility – certainty – of further discoveries. The wonders of science know no bounds – but "alternative" medicine has more in common with religion, belief in magic being no different from belief in a religious God, and I have little time for either.

Chapter Twelve
State Medical Services

People who criticise Mrs Thatcher, as she then was, for saying "There is no alternative" when referring to various economic reforms, often say the same about state-funded medical systems. At least Mrs Thatcher had evidence on her side, to judge from the economic miracle of the USA, lifting the vast majority of its population out of poverty, and the utter economic destruction of the Soviet Union, which pushed the vast majority of its population even further back into the Middle Ages.

State-funded medical services tend to decline in parallel with the Soviet experience, and for the same reason: the ideas are badly thought out in the first place. All life is political. Doctors cannot afford to believe that we can simply do our clinical work while allowing other people to do our political thinking for us.

Consider the following arguments that I first put forward in 1982:

1. **If the State takes over ultimate healthcare responsibility from the individual then:**

    a. Individuals come to think that they have rights, and hence can demand a service without at the same time having to recognise that the service is inevitably the product of the life and work and integrity of someone else.

    b. Any thinker who allows himself to be the property of someone else ceases to think. A doctor who allows himself to become merely a unit in the State provision of healthcare, rather than someone responsible for his own philosophical and mental integrity, is not worth asking the time of day, let alone his opinion on a clinical or personal problem.

    c. People assume that the State will care for the less fortunate. When presented with evidence that it does not do so, they complain that it should – but do not feel obliged to take any positive helpful action themselves. Thus the State is the cause of the Inverse Care Law, whereby those most in need of help are least likely to get it. The State creates a cruel, arid, uncaring society that smothers individual compassion and human charity. The State cannot be relied upon to produce responsible clinical care at the time that it is needed. A true sense of commitment can only be the product of an individual mind and personal philosophy. It can never be instilled by rules, regulations and committees, nor even by Royal Commissions.

2. **If resources are distributed according to need then:**

    a. People compete to establish their need rather than their capacity to do well on their own account. The individual demands his or her so-called "rights" without any thought that it is at another's expense. The corporate body, answerable for its expenditure of public funds, spends its budget up to the hilt – or even overspends, regardless of the needs of others – so that it can demand the same again or more the following year.

b. Little attention is paid to the capacity of the recipient to benefit from the resource. An absolute need may be totally unchanged even after all the resource has been devoured. Meanwhile, someone else with a lesser objective need is left with no possibility of the benefit that could have been his or hers because the resource has in effect been squandered.

c. Scientific assessment of benefit takes second place to the repetitive, mindless, arrogant hollerings of political pressure groups.

3. **If services are free at the time of need:**

   a. Perceived needs become relative rather than absolute. Meeting a need does not satisfy: it merely shifts attention to another need.

   b. Instead of the individual patient not being able to afford treatment, the State runs out of money so that either the individual cannot get treatment at all or, alternatively, the treatment that he or she can get is not worth having.

   c. The proponents of the system point to some people who have been dramatically helped "at no cost" and:

      i. play on the fear or pity of their listeners – and in doing so make them into supplicant pap;

      ii. disregard what is happening in general rather than in particular;

      iii. the State comes in time to be thought to be indispensable and with that goes every last individual freedom.

It is my own view that this theoretical model of the NHS is true in practice. Despite the excellent work that is done by many NHS doctors, nurses and other health professionals, there is no point in spending even more time and money on it. As with any failing enterprise, more expenditure of time and money simply causes it to fail even more dramatically. If the ideas and principles are wrong, the practice will inevitably fail. We should scrap the entire NHS before it causes even more suffering than it has already. In its place we should have nothing whatever other than private practice and private charity and the principles of competition and paying for quality.

Twenty years after I first wrote down these ideas I still stand by them and there is even more evidence of their truth as the NHS deteriorates even further despite numerous reorganisations and vast public financial investment. The system cannot improve whilst its basic philosophical concepts are so wildly off beam.

There certainly are other systems. The American system is certainly not all bad: the Medicare and Medicaid systems serve the elderly and the poor. The people who tend to get into difficulties in the USA tend to be those who do not come within those programmes of social welfare but who decide not to take out appropriate insurance. It is these people, often middle class and articulate, who make vociferous complaints when they fall ill and, through their own default and as a result of being above the poverty line, are not covered by either system. It is true that the poor in the USA get a fairly shoddy service – but so do the poor in the UK. Furthermore, we may complain about our immigration problem but in the USA, in addition to vast illegal immigration – mostly across the southern border – there is massive legal immigration as a result of people wanting to escape the effects of socialism and gain the benefit of capitalism. Economic research in the USA, where there is considerable social and economic mobility, has shown that the average time an individual stays below the poverty line is four months. Yet the USA has constant new responsibilities to provide medical care to new immigrants who often had little or no medical care in their countries of origin. The medical systems in Canada, Australia, France, Germany and Spain have so far been almost totally ignored by our own Department of Health on the arrogant assumption that they should learn from us. The reverse may be true.

There are many ways of providing insurance systems in which a partnership between public and private services can deliver responsible care to the whole community. However, it must be remembered that doctors will tend to turn any system to their own advantage. *The Public/Private Mix for Health*, edited by Alan Maynard and Gordon McLachlan (Nuffield Provincial Hospitals Trust 1982), reveals exactly this problem. In state systems, doctors may complain about being overworked and underpaid but they may have little insight into the real demands of the private sector and into just how hard they would have to work to make the same income as they are currently paid in the state sector. However, when the private sector is insurance-based, doctors tend to inflate their fees and put in claims for more work than they actually do. One way or another doctors will usually find something to complain about in any medical system, while at the same time milking it dry.

A particular problem in our own NHS is the confusion in doctors' minds when they believe that they are doing "good" work simply because they are not directly charging fees to patients. As a result the quality of their work may sometimes actually be rather bad. Thus, I do not believe that there is any great virtue when doctors do not charge patients for their services. The one and only virtue should be the good quality of the work that is done. Whether or not the patient directly pays the fee and is subsequently reimbursed by the Government, is an entirely separate issue. It is those alternatives that have been tried in other countries while we in the UK were left in splendid isolation in the full conviction that our system was perfect even while it progressively decayed. For the Government now to increase the expenditure on the NHS up to the level of the average European expenditure does not mean that our services will necessarily improve either to their level or even at all. While the confusion between good (virtuous) and good (quality) continues there will be no actual improvement in services to patients. The belief that good (virtuous – or even godlike) work depends simply upon the fact that patients do not pay directly for the work of doctors or other staff, is a major handicap for the future development of the NHS. It is this, rather than the level of funding, that has to be the starting point of change.

One could devise a National Health Service to function on any specific budget whatever, provided one decided what the Government should *not* provide. For example, at a certain budget we might be able to fund the treatment of cancer and heart disease and diabetes but nothing else. At a higher budgetary level we could include other medical conditions – but at each stage we should emphasise what is *not* being covered. This is where the NHS gets into trouble with budget – on never defining what it will *exclude*. The NHS currently spends £7 million a year on aspirin. Is that really necessary? Do the patients who take it really have no funds from which to buy aspirin for themselves? Is it right that our waiting lists should be so long for urgently necessary surgical or medical treatment while £7 million a year is spent solely on aspirin? These are very real questions that underline the lack of thought behind the phrase "free and comprehensive service" that has been bandied about for so many years in praise of the NHS.

Ultimately we need to ask what it is that patients should be expected to pay for. Examining the Registrar General's abstract of statistics shows us that the average family now spends more on alcohol, nicotine and gambling than it does on housing. Is this an indication of a *responsible* society? Are people really to be encouraged to expect the State to provide everything that matters rather than to make any form of provision for themselves? When the present Chancellor of the Exchequer undermines the value of private pension schemes, he sends a very clear message that thrift and responsibility for self are not worth the bother. The same message is sent when the State provides universally free health and welfare services and free education. Ultimately the population comes to be dependent upon those free services and takes no heed for itself. Again, a terrible price may ultimately be paid for something that is "free".

The possible alternative of providing charitable services for those who really cannot afford to pay for themselves, or who have no physical or mental capacity to do so, has an ambivalent position in the politics of the UK. The population at large is exceedingly supportive of charities – currently giving £13 billion a year – which shows precisely how far the general population understands that the Welfare State does *not* work well for those who most need it. At the same time, there are those who believe that "charity", with its image of Lady Bountiful, is very much a dirty word. They resent "means tests", saying that they are undignified. They prefer to have charitable services that are universally available but funded through taxation so that the rich pay for the benefit to the poor. The idea is that the State should rob Peter to pay Paul. In fact there are not sufficient Peters for this to happen. The major taxation revenue comes from people on middle rather than high incomes. Therefore what really happens in practice is that the State robs Paul, mucks around at great expense and then gives Paul back less than he had in the first place.

Perhaps things really go wrong in the NHS because the State is both the paymaster and the provider. It might be better for these processes to become progressively more separated so that the State pays for services from private companies who compete with each other to provide clinical services. This already happens in many ancillary services such as catering and cleaning. There is no clinical or ethically justifiable reason why the process should not cover the entire range of NHS services.

Recently a transport trade union leader pointed out that the country could not do without the services of his members and therefore he felt perfectly justified in demanding more pay for less work on his members' behalf. It was refreshing to find a trade unionist being so honest in this respect. The British Medical Association and other medical Trade Unions will doubtless not be slow in taking this leaf out of his book. What the attitude of this particular trade union leader illustrates is that a major part of left-wing philosophy is not at all directed towards the good of the country at large or towards those people whose need is greatest and who have the least capacity to help themselves. It rewards industrial muscle. In this it is no different from the right-wing extreme that rewards company directors for their industrial muscle – sometimes irrespective of whether their actions truly benefit their shareholders' interests.

The UK seems therefore to exhibit an extraordinary paradox: considerable personal generosity in donations to charities coupled with equally considerable institutional greed and social disregard. The leaders of various institutions may think themselves to be gods but it is the individuals who actually show personal care for other people who are less well off than themselves. It is these generous private individuals – from all walks of life – who are the real gods.

Chapter Thirteen

Bureaucracy

The British Civil Service has a noble history but it has in many ways gone to seed. Government officers who successfully ran an empire have sometimes been superseded by those who could not run a church tea party.

"Colonialism" is now a dirty word but I wonder how many of the common people in former colonies would now gladly give up their "independence" - which appears to be indistinguishable from tyranny. There were many colonial abuses but there were also considerable benefits, and it is inappropriate for these to be overlooked in an orgy of national guilt.

The present Civil Service mostly administers only our own tiny islands but often still has the airs and graces of its internationalist forebears even though they seem almost completely to lack the vision and talent. The recent BSE crisis was totally mishandled and caused terrible destruction to our beef industry while having negligible influence upon the incidence of Creutzfeldt-Jakob disease in human beings. The foot and mouth crisis devastated our farming industry and also the much larger tourism industry and we are still left wondering whether vaccination or slaughter or some other policy altogether would be best. Is it not the function of bureaucrats to know the answer to these questions?

The AIDS epidemic has not appeared in the dramatic numbers that were predicted even though illegitimate pregnancies (indicating un-safe sexual activity) continue as before. Listeria has not swept the country and the only legacy of that scare is advice that pregnant women should avoid eating soft cheeses. Legionella has not devastated all office buildings even though it does occasionally break out in some. However, the bureaucrats had to get something right eventually, simply by dint of numbers of crises, and they appear to have done so in countering the inappropriate concerns over the combined measles/mumps/rubella vaccine being linked to autism. There is no evidence of any stature that the MMR vaccine may lead to autism, and the alternative of single vaccines is not providing a sufficient pool of immunity in the population for these significant diseases to be kept under control. To get just one issue right is a very poor rate of return for the trust - and money - given to our Civil Service. Did any heads roll? I certainly do not remember them doing so.

Power without responsibility seems now to be the prerogative of the Civil Service rather than of politicians or of the oldest profession in the world - and as the responsibility diminishes, their power often increases.

These are the tin gods who run the country even though the politicians rule it. Politicians create the larger picture but the nitty-gritty of every-day life, when the population at large come across Government legislation that affects them, is largely in the hands of bureaucrats. It is the interpretation of the law and its nit-picking implementation that causes such widespread distress and absolute exasperation.
Bureaucrats play perpetual "pass the parcel" and are terrified that they will be caught out when the music stops. Their concern is primarily to avoid blame landing

on themselves. They dare not take a reasonable view: they cannot afford the possibility of something going wrong, of finding themselves in court being cross-examined by a hostile barrister on precisely why they may have interpreted the law in a particular way. Thus the blame for the progressive stifling bureaucratisation of our country, which becomes more Soviet in its red tape every day, lies as much with lawyers and parliamentarians as with the bureaucrats themselves. But the Civil Service appears to have become so emasculated that it lacks the courage to speak up for itself and always seeks not only the shelter of anonymity but also the path of least resistance: total freedom from blame. It is only from this perspective that one can have any sympathy whatever with the bureaucrats' behaviour: they have nothing to gain and therefore they do not see why they should risk losing their own pensions by taking chances.

The problem is that this cripples the rest of us, particularly those who are trying to do anything creative. We are seen as a threat. However much politicians may pay lip service to an enterprise culture and the need to stimulate small business, the bureaucracy – and the banks – do everything they possibly can to put us into the ground.

For example, the first year of operation of the PROMIS Recovery Centre was a financial disaster. We had previously spent a whole year in trying to raise charitable funds to build a treatment centre but we raised absolutely no money whatever. My wife and I therefore re-mortgaged our home and our medical practice and established the treatment centre. In the first year, while receiving many brickbats for "making profits from the sick", we actually lost a thousand pounds a day. We survived only through the generous understanding and forbearance of our suppliers.

In due course my wife and I moved down to the basement of our home and moved twelve patients into the living rooms and bedrooms that we had vacated: the basement was really a coal hole and had been used for storage. The patients were those who had completed treatment in the inpatient centre and were now gradually finding their feet back in the real world in central London. They lived with us and had counselling support for half the day but for the other half they went out to work or to training programmes or otherwise got themselves involved in preparing for the final transition back to full responsibility for self.

Our premises were registered with the social services and all went well for five years. Then the social services decided that they should apply the same criteria to bedroom sizes as were applicable to nursing homes. This meant that we would inevitably lose one third of our beds and we could not possibly fund the patients' treatment at that level. I pointed out that our patients were fit and healthy and that they spent part of every week in sporting activities – an uncommon endeavour in nursing homes. I also pointed out that the patients' bedrooms were used solely for sleep rather than as living accommodation, and that if the patients were caught in the bedrooms during the day they would have to be highly creative with their explanations. All this evidence of the real life situation was to no avail: the regulations had to be obeyed. We therefore had no choice but to close down that establishment. I pointed out to the social services that they had thereby achieved the bureaucrats' idea of paradise: ours was the only "halfway house" in the borough and therefore there would now be nothing left for the bureaucrats to supervise – but the regulations would have been obeyed.

I also pointed out that the accommodation that we provided for our patients was of a much higher standard – and less crowded – than that in which many of them had ever lived before, or was generally available to the local population in North Kensington. Again, these arguments fell on deaf ears: the regulations had to be obeyed.

The Care Standards Act 2000 and its implementation by the National Care Standards Commission is currently in danger of destroying the country's stock of nursing homes. On the virtuous principle of improving standards (as established and implemented by bureaucrats), old people's homes are disappearing at an alarming rate and many acute beds in hospitals are being blocked by elderly people who are too infirm to return to their own homes and now have nowhere else to go. I am not arguing that standards should not be maintained and improved, but I do believe that the standards that are set are often totally unrealistic in respect of the economic viability of the nursing homes or other organisations in question. But since when did bureaucrats understand economic viability? They themselves are salaried and they are totally averse to risk. They would not understand the first principle of running a business: that they would have to make a profit or close.

In trying to improve standards, they are in fact lowering them by reducing the number of facilities available and discouraging other people from entering the market. I use the term "market" deliberately because all healthcare is a market, whether it is paid for by government or privately, and market principles have to apply. When the state runs out of money, it closes beds and reduces services – exactly as happens in the private sector. I fear that the product of the work of the National Care Standards Commission will be the same as that of other Government-sponsored administrative organisations: the people who are most in need of help will be the ones who are least likely to receive it. This "Inverse Care Law" was first formulated by Dr Julian Tudor Hart, a GP working in South Wales. He saw his law as a challenge to Government to provide more services. I see it as a direct result of Government services. Government destroys initiative. Protocols impede as well as guide. Threats are utterly destructive. "Ve haf ways of making you compassionate" does not convince.

"Ve haf ways of making you competent" is equally unconvincing when applied by the National Institute for Clinical Excellence. Competence is more an emotional than intellectual function: it disintegrates when doctors become fed up and lose interest, not because they mysteriously lose their capacity to think. There is nothing mysterious about it: when doctors cease to do good work, it is because their minds are on something else – usually on what they might be able to do if they were to leave the profession altogether. The NHS is in big trouble as a result of the sheer number of doctors choosing to retire early. It will be in even bigger trouble if the extraordinarily high number of doctors who are currently in their thirties carry out their expressed intention to retire from the profession before they are fifty. This level of disillusion cannot be corrected with the use of sticks and carrots: it needs a fundamental reappraisal of the relationship between Government and the doctors and other staff who work for it. To be monitored is fine when one is also supported and encouraged. To be monitored and controlled is something else altogether: fascism. That is a very ungodly philosophy.

false medical gods

Chapter Fourteen

The One True God

The irony of religious zealots who believe in "one true God" is that these gods are so numerous. If only the zealots who adhere to a particular faith could look at others who adhere to another and recognise that they might both be wrong! The same principle applies to anyone who attacks other people's ideas – as I do myself. *I may be wrong*. Certainly, "Robert Lefever" would be a totally inappropriate god for me myself or for anyone else. As someone who has an addictive nature, I know only too well what happened when I had unshakeable beliefs: I ran my life into the ground. The "one true God" in which I now believe is not a person but an idea: individualism, the respect for people as themselves, right or wrong as I may consider them, rather than as members of any social, political, racial, financial or other group.

To this end, I have profound respect for the Objectivist Oath of Ayn Rand:

"I swear, by my life and my love of it,
that I shall never live for the sake of another man
nor ask that he shall live for mine."

On this principle, I do not follow meekly as one of a herd, nor do I expect other people to do and say only what I decree. I respect and value my own life and the principles by which I live and therefore I also respect other people's. I respect their right to disagree with me. Further, I hope that they will disagree with me at times because that is the only way that I shall learn – by seeing where my own ideas could be improved. For example, I remember my mother once despairingly asking me when I would have the same ideas two years in a row. I replied that I hoped I never would.

On this principle of individualism I have built my own personal and professional life. My wife and I stay with each other because we want to – not because we have a certificate to prove that we are married, nor because we believe that we could never be attracted to anyone else. I do the work that I want to do and I stop doing it when I find that I do not enjoy it any more. I make choices. I do not belong to anyone else. Correspondingly, I accept other people's right to make their own choices, provided that these are not at the expense of someone else's rights.

It was on that precise principle that I stopped working for the NHS. Things were obviously not going to get better; there was no way that they could do so on the philosophical principles upon which it is based. Despite the very considerable work that I had done in creating a group medical practice, I resigned from it. Subsequently I resigned from the NHS altogether when I recognised that there was no chance of influencing it in its big ideas or on the specific issue of having simple diagnostic facilities in general practice. There may be a chance now of achieving that through some form of public/private partnership – but I resigned more than twenty years ago. I had done my very best to influence the ideas of the Department of Health and the British Medical Association and the Royal College of General Practitioners, in which I was the education secretary for the South London faculty. However, it was quite clear that I was not going to win these battles. I was merely a cog in a dysfunctional monolithic wheel. Massive structures – state or private – eventually run themselves into the ground when they disregard individuals and force them into corporate moulds. I became impatient to put my own ideas into practice rather than wait until other people came round to them. That surely is the driving force of innovation and creativity upon which progress depends in any sphere of human activity. We co-operate with each other in putting ideas into practice but we have to leave space for originality to express itself in the first place.

I believe that, on the principle of individualism, it was inevitable that I would have a wonderful professional life and indeed I have. I do not achieve this at other people's expense. I take my own risks and I make a determined contribution to wider society in my work. I would go out of business if I were not to do so. I am still in full-time work, doing a seven-day week as I have done for the last seventeen years, sharing the time between my medical practice and the Counselling Centre in London during the week and the Recovery Centre in Kent at the weekends. My two junior partners from the NHS group practice both became progressively more disillusioned and have now retired in order to do something else.

We are losing the enthusiasm of our medical profession. No medical system on earth can afford that loss. In the UK National Health Service, the administrative centralised control results in the achievement of the lowest common denominator rather than the highest common factor. The platoon marches at the pace of its slowest member and all the rest are held back. That principle may work for the army on the drill square – although I suspect it does not work like that when under fire in open warfare. It certainly cannot work in the NHS or in any business. We have to be led by innovation rather than conformity. We have to search for new ideas and better ways of doing things. We have to compete with each other so that the ideas that succeed are those that are proven in the crucible of real life. We can listen to people's words but we should judge them on their actions: speeches are great but successful demonstration is better. We look for solutions that really do help the poor and needy, disabled and disadvantaged, rather than impose ideas that superficially sound good in theory but which do not work in practice.

Above all, we have to be prepared to make mistakes: to get things wrong, acknowledge that we have done so, and learn from the experience. The only way to make no mistakes is to do nothing at all – but that is the worst mistake of all, the complete negation of life itself. Progress comes when we recognise that perfection is impossible. We are not gods. However, each one of us can do our best individually each day of our lives. In so doing we get closer to the God within us – our enthusiasm (Greek, en theos: God within). We show our caring through our professionalism and through the creativity that drives us forward each day. If the State is to be involved in education, health, welfare or any other enterprise, then it should be on behalf of specific individuals, paying for their care through the purchase of services from competing providers, never as an employer. That emperor has no clothes.

In the private healthcare sector we make profits from the sick because it is a worthy cause to do so. In the private sector we look after the sick because we are dedicated to their care just as the vast majority of NHS doctors and other healthcare professionals are dedicated to the care of the sick. We make profits because we have a right to be paid for our work and because we wish to remain independent. We ask for no handouts and we have to provide a service that patients value more than they value the services of others with whom we compete. We charge fees that people – sometimes NHS authorities – are prepared to pay. We stand or fall on the quality of the service we offer. We allow our own and other people's failed ideas to go to the wall because there is no point in following what theoretically might appear to be a good idea if it does not work in practice. Bailing out the failures damages everything else, especially the tender growing points of new ideas and new practices. We have courage and take risks when we believe that something is right.

At the end of our lives we are grateful for the opportunities that we have been given and for the privilege of having been able to do what we can to help others. As Ayn Rand pointed out in her Objectivist Oath, we do not live for the sake of other people nor ask them to live for ours: it is our own spirits that drive us and that is what gives us the capacity to be genuinely helpful to others. If that was not our motive, then why on earth would we ever have become doctors or nurses or other healthcare workers in the first place? There are easier ways of earning a living but no more rewarding profession on God's earth. If caring for others was our motive but it has been driven out by the NHS, then we have to say the same words that Oliver Cromwell used when addressing the Rump Parliament: "You have sat too long here for any good you have been doing. Depart, I say, and let us have done with you. In the name of God go!".

false medical gods

Other books in the series

Preventing Addiction

Cigarette Smoking. Fifteen reasons for continuing to smoke (or not)

Dangerous Doctors

Healing

Common Sense in the Treatment of Eating Disorders

Spiritual Awakening. Working the Twelve Step programme

Inside the Madness

How to Combat Alcoholism and Addiction

How to Combat Anorexia, Bulimia and Compulsive Overeating

Spirituality for Atheists and Agnostics

A New Life. Healing depression

Compulsive Helping

Healthy Relationships

Prescription Drug Addiction. My doctor gave it to me

Behavioural Addictions: Workaholism. Shopaholism. Exercise Addiction. Gambling and Risk Taking. Self-Harming. Obsessive Compulsive Disorder

Detoxification and Harm Minimisation

Childhood Abuse and Abandonment

Healing Emotional Trauma with E.M.D.R.

Healing Emotional Trauma with Psychodrama

Treating Chronic Relapse. Not again

Help: The Dairy of a Private Doctor

- **Vol 1: I will *not* make do.** The philosophy and politics of help
- **Vol 2: Daughters are Difficult.** Professional help in clinical practice
- **Vol 3: Henry is a Good Man.** The boundaries of help
- **Vol 4: Robin's turn.** Beyond help